I Love to Read

Fun Reading Projects
Recommended by Kids

Michelle O'Brien-Palmer

illustrations by
Heidi Stephens

MicNik Publications, Inc.

Credits

Illustrations:	Heidi Stephens
Front Cover Art:	Denny Driver
Back Cover Layout:	Michelle O'Brien-Palmer
Copy Editors:	Lory Hess
	Gid Palmer

Content Editors:
Martha Ivy's students, Christa McAuliffe Elementary, Lake Washington Schools, Redmond, WA
Nancy Johnston's students, Wilder Elementary, Lake Washington Schools, Woodinville, WA
Valerie Marshall's students, Christa McAuliffe Elementary, Lake Washington Schools, Redmond, WA
Pam Schild's students, Wilder Elementary, Woodinville, WA
Nancie Schonhard's students, Wilder Elementary, Woodinville, WA
Joyce Standing's students, The Overlake School, Redmond, WA

Other Contributors:
Stefanie Garcia, 6th-grade student, Wilder Elementary, Woodinville, WA
Ann Lyman, teacher, Westhill Elementary, Northshore Schools, Bothell, WA
Julee Neupert, teacher, Ben Rush Elementary, Lake Washington Schools, Redmond, WA
Eileen Shaner, teacher, Franconia Elementary, Souderton School District, Souderton, PA
Alesha Thomas, 6th-grade student, Wilder Elementary, Woodinville, WA

Young Authors:

Kadi Anderson	Jenny Jones	Nick Palmer
Eunice Chung	Janet Kim	Brian Schnierer
Tierney Creech	Kristina Lin	Broderick Smith
Carey DeAngelis	Justin Lobdell	Sandy Stonesifer
Colby Emerson	Edward Lobdell	Michael Strong
Emily Gibbons	Greg Lundwall	Terry Yoo
Hannah Gibbons	Matt Marcoe	Steven Yoo
Meghan Gibbons	Andy Meade	Christi Warren
Lisa Hails	Willie Nelson	Jamie Weaver
Chris Hartsell	Tara O'Brien	Jackie White
Billy Harris	Sean O'Connor	

ISBN 1-879235-06-4
Library of Congress Catalog Card Number: 95-94139
Copyright © 1995 Michelle O'Brien-Palmer

Manufactured in the United States of America

10 9 8 7 6 5 4 3 2 1

ATTENTION: SCHOOLS AND BUSINESSES

Books from MicNik Publications, Inc., are available at quantity discounts with bulk purchase
for educational, business, or sales promotional use. For information, please write, call or fax:
MicNik Publications, Inc.
P.O. Box 3041, Kirkland, WA 98083
(206) 881-6476 – fax (206) 885-2133

Acknowledgements

I would like to thank the following people for their support and contributions in the creation of *I Love to Read*.

I am especially grateful to the 6th-grade editors for your honest feedback, project recommendations and inspiration for *I Love to Read*. In our seven months together, you made significant contributions in molding *I Love to Read* into its final form. I am very proud to have had the opportunity to work through the writing process with you as my editors.

- Thanks to the student editors from Nancy Johnston's class at Wilder Elementary School. Your project ideas and examples were wonderful. I really appreciate your sharing them with the readers of this book.
- Thanks to the student editors from Pam Schild's class at Wilder Elementary School. Your responsible attitude and great ideas really made a difference in this book.
- Thanks to the student editors from Nancie Schonhard's class at Wilder Elementary School. Your suggestions for material lists at the end of the chapters, organizing forms and materials will help the readers of this book immensely. Thanks for your editorial suggestions on the index.

I also extend sincere thanks to those who helped in the production of this book:

To the young authors for their project examples – Kadi Anderson, Eunice Chung, Tierney Creech, Carey DeAngelis, Colby Emerson, Emily Gibbons, Hannah Gibbons, Meghan Gibbons, Lisa Hails, Billy Harris, Jenny Jones, Janet Kim, Kristina Lin, Justin Lobdell, Edward Lobdell, Greg Lundwall, Matt Marcoe, Andy Meade, Willie Neslon, Tara O'Brien, Sean O'Connor, Nick Palmer, Brian Schnierer, Broderick Smith, Sandy Stonesifer, Michael Strong, Terry Yoo, Steven Yoo, Christi Warren, Jamie Weaver, and Jackie White. To Stefanie Garcia and Alesha Thomas for their great project ideas.

To the students in Valerie Marshall's and Martha Ivy's class at McAuliffe Elementary – thank you for inviting me into your classroom. I had such fun talking with you and sharing the process of writing this book. I really appreciate special effort you made to help me problem solve.

To the students in Joyce Standing's class at The Overlake School – you are so enthusiastic and excited about reading and writing it was inspiring to be among you. Thank you for sharing your projects.

To Martha Ivy, Ann Lyman, Nancy Johnston, Valerie Marshall, Julee Neupert, Eileen Shaner, Pam Schild, Nancie Schonhard, and Joyce Standing for sharing your project ideas.

To Heidi Stephens for your wonderfully inspired illustrations, to Denny Driver for your bright cover design, to Lory Hess for your professional editing, and to Jennifer Mays for your help with the book index.

To Evelyn Sansky for your constant love and friendship, to my son, Nick Palmer for your hugs, patience, and writing samples, and to my husband, Gid Palmer for your love and support through all of my creative endeavors.

i LOVE TO READ

is **dedicated** to every child involved in this book

Students from Pam Schild's Class

Melissa Bernard
Cassie Bolin
Carey DeAngelis
Caitlin Endres
Stefanie Garcia
Jessica Gregson

Jeff Hill
Krissy Shea
Blake Skouras
Michael Strong
Craig Swanson
Alesha Thomas

Young Authors

Kadi Anderson
Eunice Chung
Tierney Creech
Carey DeAngelis
Colby Emerson
Emily Gibbons
Hannah Gibbons
Meghan Gibbons
Lisa Hails
Billy Harris
Chris Hartsell

Jenny Jones
Janet Kim
Kristina Lin
Justin Lobdell
Edward Lobdell
Greg Lundwall
Matt Marcoe
Andy Meade
Willie Nelson
Tara O'Brien
Sean O'Connor

Nick Palmer
Brian Schnierer
Broderick Smith
Sandy Stonesifer
Michael Strong
Terry Yoo
Steven Yoo
Christi Warren
Jamie Weaver
Jackie White

Students from Nancie Schonhard's Class

Zach Barth
Samson Chiang
T.C. Colleran
Tierney Creech
Reggie Green
Jay Hellenga
Jenny Jones

P.J. Kapsales
Dustin Marshall
Justin Matts
Luke Myers
David Stolowitz
Jackie White

Students from Nancy Johnston's Class

Kadi Anderson
Nathan Belt
Lisa Hails
Janet Kim
Greg Lundwall
Willie Nelson
Sean O'Connor
Christi Warren

Valerie Marshall's and Martha Ivy's Students

Taylor Bass
Dana Bentsen
Andrew Blair
Meghan Blume
Bernie Boglioli
Kaitlyn Bolduc
Jamie Boscow
Chris Brown
Carey Cade
Kaitlin Carbrey
Michael Chealander
Annie Chiu
Julie Culleton
Jordan Davidoff
Jennifer Dickens
Stephanie Diers

Matt Farrington
Andrea Geary
Justin Gedney
Meryl Goodwin
Matthew Hecker
Brady Johnson
Jenny Keaton
Matthew Kesl
Shawn Kidd
Michael Kilburg
Megan Kilkelly
Melissa Kowalchuk
Jessee Kubitz
Nick Landi
Brian Leierzapf
Sean Logue
Katharine Mackey

Elise McKinney
Vimombi Nshom
Pat O'Leary
Jeremy Peronto
Casey Peterson
Nick Ramsey
Robert Reimer
Katie Rooney
Ryan Shane
Kelsey Sikma
Stephanie Sinclair
Michael Slaughter
Conor Thurman
Jake Vela
Erin Whittington
Kaitlin Wight

Students from Joyce Standing's Class

Michelle Bauer
Eunice Chung
Colby Emerson
Billy Harris
Diane Jenkins
Peter Johnson
Kristina Lin
Matt Marcoe
Mark Mavis

Andy Meade
Darcy Milne
Broderick Smith
Shon Smith
Sandy Stonesifer
Kacie Tomlinson
Evan Tuck
Chrissy Wakeling
Jamie Weaver

Table of Contents

PROJECT RECIPES: Chapter 6

REFERENCE BOOKS: Chapter 7

FORMS TO COPY: Chapter 8

PROJECT INDEX: Chapter 9

PROJECT INDEX: Chapter 9 (Continued)

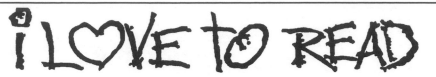

Introduction

for parents and teachers

I LOVE TO READ: **Fun Reading Projects Recommended by Kids** is written to give children (K-6th grade) a diverse selection of reading extension projects they can create in celebration of the books they are reading. This text is the fourth in a whole language series, which includes *Book-Write: A Creative Bookmaking Guide for Young Authors*, *Book-Talk: Exciting Literature Experiences for Kids* and *Read & Write: Fun Literature and Writing Connections for Kids*.

This book was written at the request of teachers from all over the country. They knew of individual reading extension projects but really wanted a resource which pulled together many different projects. For your convenience, *I LOVE TO READ* was organized into character, setting and plot projects. However, the index provides many other ways of categorizing projects. Each project was recommended and tested by kids. An example is provided for every project.

Although the text speaks to children directly, it will require adult supervision and guidance in most cases. There are projects which need an exacto knife, scissors and sometimes require ovens or stoves. Many chapters include two front pages with a visual representation of each project. This is to help kids see what the projects look like and and then look up the projects which they find the most interesting. Whenever extra information might be helpful to parents or teachers it will be found in italics just under the top border of a text page. The second chapter (Keeping Track) includes a number of organizing forms for books, projects and materials. There is also a chapter of forms for you to use with your children at home or school. Make as many copies as you need of these forms as well as any blank forms you find in other chapters. The resource chapter at the end of the book is intended to provide a list of excellent references for bringing literature into the home or classroom.

Each project idea in this book is meant to be taken as liberally as possible. There is no one right way to do anything. The more variations created, the more exciting the process will be.

I LOVE TO READ

Foreword
Note to Kids

I love to read! The kids who helped me write *I LOVE TO READ* enjoy reading too. We decided to create a book which celebrates reading and shares our favorite reading projects with you. We worked together for seven months in a school library which looks much like the front illustration; we shared project ideas, tested those ideas, and finally came up with our list of favorite projects. We hope you enjoy these projects as much as we do.

The chapter called Keeping Track was designed to help you organize your project materials and keep track of the books you read and the projects you complete. We also included a project materials list at the back of each project chapter. You can copy them and use them to gather your project supplies.

The projects are listed in a number of ways through the index. Check the index for categories which might help you decide just the right project for the book you are reading.

Some projects will be new to you and some may be similar to projects you've made before. Use your imagination to create your own unique projects.

Have fun celebrating your favorite books!

Chapter 1

Introduction

Introduction to I Love to Read:
Fun Reading Projects Recommended by Kids

This chapter provides a brief introduction to each main chapter. *I Love to Read* was written with the help of over 100 kids. They were part of the writing and editing process. The young authors who share their unedited examples of projects in the book are listed below:

Kadi Anderson	Janet Kim	Brian Schnierer
Eunice Chung	Kristina Lin	Broderick Smith
Tierney Creech	Justin Lobdell	Sandy Stonesifer
Carey DeAngelis	Edward Lobdell	Michael Strong
Colby Emerson	Greg Lundwall	Terry Yoo
Emily Gibbons	Matt Marcoe	Steven Yoo
Hannah Gibbons	Andy Meade	Christi Warren
Meghan Gibbons	Willie Nelson	Jamie Weaver
Lisa Hails	Tara O'Brien	Jackie White
Billy Harris	Sean O'Connor	
Jenny Jones	Nick Palmer	

Chapter 2: Keeping Track

This chapter is set up to help readers organize and track their books, projects, and project materials. The *book train* and *reading bookworm* are fun formats which allow younger readers an opportunity to proudly display the books they have read. The *book chain* and *goal sheet* help more experienced readers set reading goals and track their progress. The *track a project sheets* are categorized by character, setting, and plot. They give readers instant feedback as to the types of projects they have created. The *checklist of project decorating items* and the *materials list* are great tools for setting up an area with materials you'll need to create the projects in *I Love To Read*.

Chapter 3: Character Projects

The projects in this chapter allow readers to explore story characters more fully. Younger children can start with identifying the characters in the story by making a simple *accordion book*. Creating *sponge characters* or *character sculptures* naturally facilitates readers retelling a story through the eyes of the characters. The *talking character, pop-up dialogue* and *thumbprint character* projects are great introductions to writing dialogue. The *biography monologue*, *meet the character* and *story flip book* projects give readers an opportunity to do a more in-depth analysis of story characters.

Chapter 4: Setting Projects

Setting is not always an easy concept to grasp. The setting projects in this chapter are intended to help make this concept more concrete. This chapter's projects range in complexity from simple *story stones* to the creation of a *story neighborhood* made of milk cartons, boxes and other recycled items. Readers can travel through the story setting on a *magnetic story map* they draw themselves. Using *dioramas*, a *triorama* or a *shoebox story scene*, readers can create a scene right out of the story. *Story props*, *story snow scenes*, and *storyboards* become lively additions to any book-talk, book report or story retelling.

Chapter 5: Plot Projects

The first plot project is a card book younger children can make to identify a story's *beginning, middle, and end*. Retelling a story is another way of identifying the story's plot. Many of the projects in this chapter are based upon the identification of key events important in the retelling of a story. These projects will enhance any retelling; *story time capsule, story pop-out, story retell poster, candy box retell, first-person journal, story banner* and *story box*. In addition, the *story pop-out, fold-a-story, story cube, story newsletter* and *non-fiction shape book* can all stand alone as alternatives to standard book reports.

Chapter 6: Project Recipes

This chapter houses recipes for many different projects. The recipes provide how-to information in making various materials and books recommended for certain chapter projects.

Chapter 9: Project Index

The index lists projects in categories for easy project selection. Check this index to determine the best application for your needs.

Chapter 2

Keeping Track

Track a Book

Book Train

page 20

Reading Bookworm

page 22

Book Chain

page 24

Track a Project

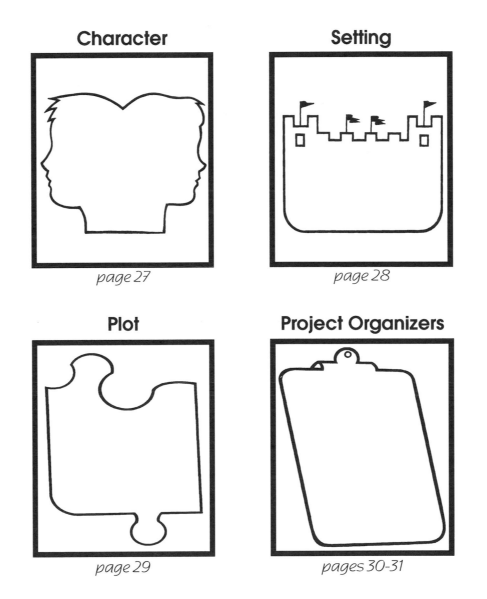

Character

page 27

Setting

page 28

Plot

page 29

Project Organizers

pages 30-31

Book Train

The book train is a fun way younger readers can proudly display the books they have read.

Materials:

Colored paper	Scissors
Forms (copy – page 144)	Pencil/crayons
Laminating materials	Glue

Goal:

To keep track of the books you've read in a train you can display

Steps:

1. Make a copy of the train forms (page 144).
2. Draw yourself in the train engine.
3. Write the book title and the date you finished reading the book inside the train car. Draw your favorite character in the window.
4. Glue the car and engine together.
5. Each time you read another book fill out a train car.
6. Hang up the book train in your room.

Book Train Examples

Reading Bookworm

A reading bookworm is another way to record the books you've read. Primary grade children love this project.

Materials:

Colored cardstock	Scissors
Form (copy – page 23)	Hole punch
Laminating materials	Ring

Goal:

To keep track of the books you've read

Steps:

1. Copy bookworm form on colored cardstock.
2. Cut out one of the bookworms.
3. Write your name, the book title and the date you finished reading the book inside the bookworm.
4. Laminate the bookworm.
5. Punch a hole in the eye section.
6. Place your completed bookworm on a ring.
7. Each time you read a book fill out a worm.
8. Share the bookworms with your friends.

Bookworm Form

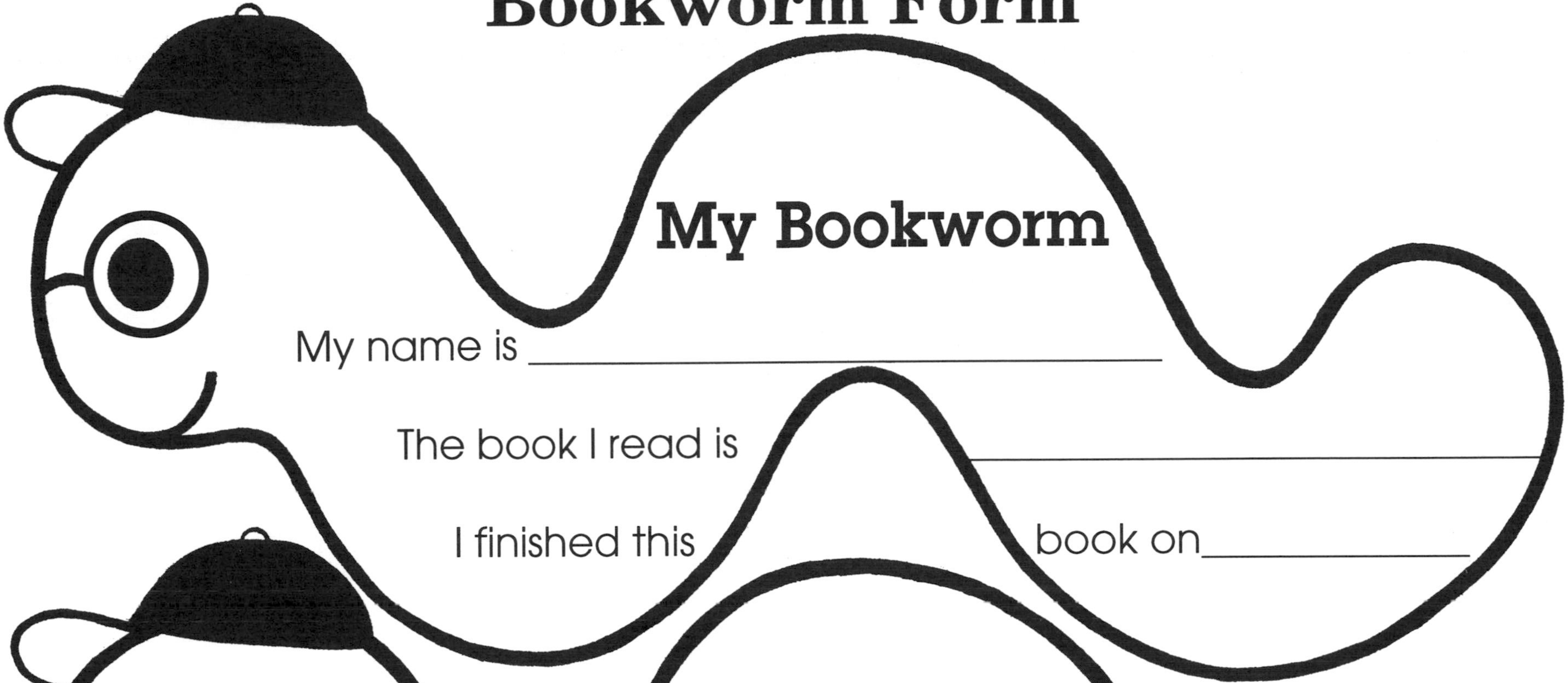

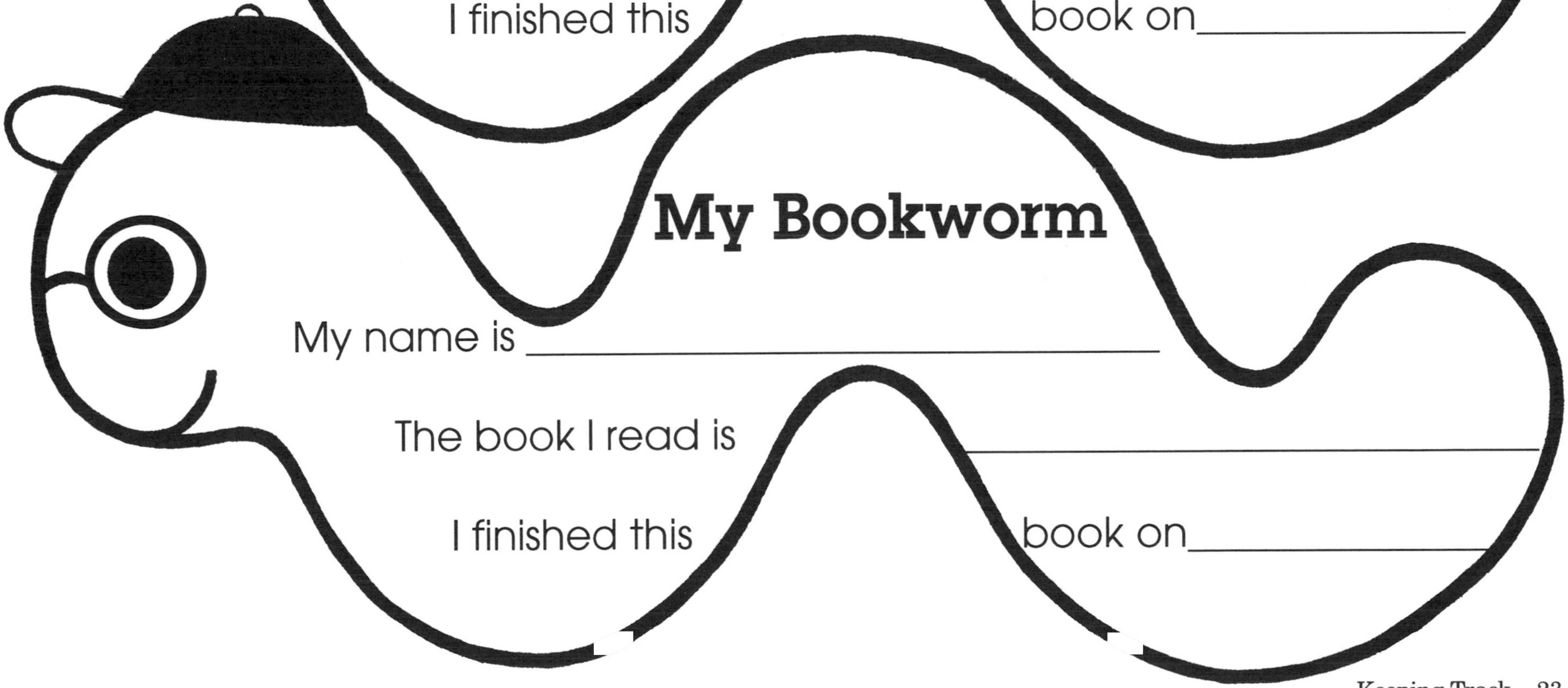

My Bookworm

My name is _____

The book I read is _____

I finished this   book on_____

My Bookworm

My name is _____

The book I read is _____

I finished this   book on_____

Book Chain

The book chain idea came from 6th-graders Alesha Thomas and Stefanie Garcia. They suggest hanging the chains in your room or using them for decorations at holidays.

Materials:

Colored/white paper   Markers/pencil

Forms (copy – page 22)   Glue stick

Scissors

Goal:

To display a chain of book titles you've read

Steps:

1. Determine the number of book titles you want to include on your chain.
2. Copy the goal form and fill it out.
3. Copy the chain form using colored paper.
4. Read the book you've selected.
5. When you've finished reading, fill out a chain form and cut it out.
6. Hook the ends around the last link and glue to form another link in your chain.

Book Chain Forms

Book Chain Goal Sheet

Today's Date:

Name:

Number of books I want to read and include in my chain _____.

Starting date _____   Goal ending date _____

Types of books (genres) I want to include:

❏ Adventure	❏ Fairytale	❏ Historical Fiction	❏ Science Fiction
❏ Biography	❏ Fantasy	❏ Mystery	❏ Realistic Fiction
❏ Courage and Survival	❏ Humor	❏ Poetry	❏ Other:_____

Title: _____   **Title:** _____

Author: _____   **Author:** _____

Title: _____   **Title:** _____

Author: _____   **Author:** _____

Title: _____   **Title:** _____

Author: _____   **Author:** _____

Track a Project Sheets

These sheets help kids monitor and evaluate the projects they have completed. For fast tracking, kids recommend color coding each type of project.

Materials:
Forms (copy – page 145,146,147)

Scissors   Pencil/pen

Ring   Hole punch

Laminating materials

Goal:
To keep track of the different kinds of projects you've created

Steps:
1. Use colored paper to copy the form that fits the project you completed.
2. Cut out the form and write the project title and book title inside.
3. Did you enjoy making this project? Check the box that that fits your answer. Then laminate the project sheet.
4. Punch a hole in the circle at the bottom of the sheet. Place the sheet on a ring.
5. Share your favorite projects with friends.

Character Project Sheet Example

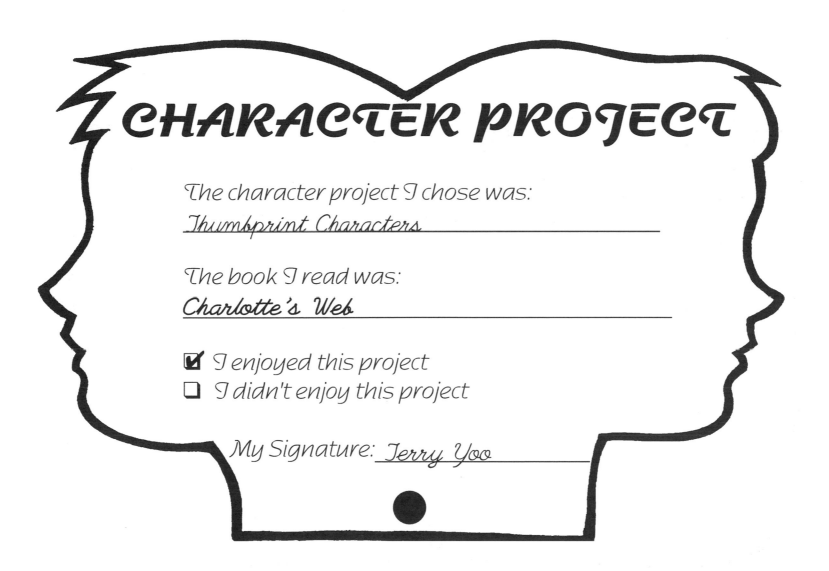

CHARACTER PROJECT

The character project I chose was:
Thumbprint Characters

The book I read was:
Charlotte's Web

☑ I enjoyed this project
☐ I didn't enjoy this project

My Signature: *Jerry Yoo*

Setting Project Sheet Example

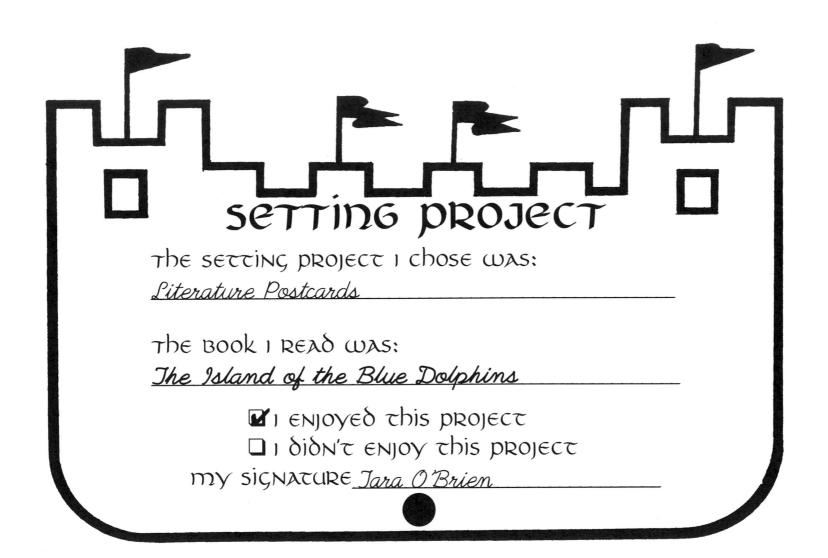

SETTING PROJECT

THE SETTING PROJECT I CHOSE WAS:

Literature Postcards

THE BOOK I READ WAS:

The Island of the Blue Dolphins

☑ I ENJOYED THIS PROJECT
☐ I DIDN'T ENJOY THIS PROJECT

MY SIGNATURE *Tara O'Brien*

Plot Project Sheet Example

PLOT PROJECT

THE PLOT PROJECT I CHOSE WAS:

Candy Box Retell

THE BOOK I READ WAS:

A Little Princess

☑ I ENJOYED THIS PROJECT
☐ I DIDN'T ENJOY THIS PROJECT

MY SIGNATURE: *Meghan Gibbons*

Checklist of Project Decorating Items

- ❑ aluminum foil
- ❑ beads
- ❑ beans
- ❑ bottle caps
- ❑ brads
- ❑ buttons
- ❑ cans
- ❑ cardboard
- ❑ cardboard tubes
- ❑ clay
- ❑ colored moss
- ❑ colored paper
- ❑ colored pencils
- ❑ colored plastic wrap
- ❑ computer paper
- ❑ construction paper
- ❑ cookie cutters
- ❑ cotton balls (colored)
- ❑ crepe paper
- ❑ drinking straws
- ❑ egg cartons
- ❑ fabric paint
- ❑ fabric scraps
- ❑ feathers
- ❑ felt squares
- ❑ film containers

- ❑ finger paints
- ❑ glitter
- ❑ glue stick
- ❑ googly eyes
- ❑ hangers
- ❑ lace
- ❑ magazines
- ❑ margarine tubs
- ❑ markers
- ❑ milk cartons
- ❑ newspapers
- ❑ plain paper
- ❑ paper clips
- ❑ paper cups
- ❑ paper plates
- ❑ paper scraps
- ❑ pastels
- ❑ pencil
- ❑ pens
- ❑ pie tins
- ❑ pipe cleaners
- ❑ play dough
- ❑ popsicle sticks
- ❑ Q-tips
- ❑ ribbon
- ❑ sand

- ❑ shells
- ❑ spices
- ❑ sponges
- ❑ spools
- ❑ stickers
- ❑ string
- ❑ tagboard pieces
- ❑ tissue paper
- ❑ toothpicks
- ❑ twigs
- ❑ wallpaper pieces
- ❑ wire
- ❑ wood scraps
- ❑ wrapping paper
- ❑ yarn
- ❑ _____
- ❑ _____
- ❑ _____
- ❑ _____
- ❑ _____
- ❑ _____
- ❑ _____
- ❑ _____
- ❑ _____
- ❑ _____
- ❑ _____

Material List

for the projects in *I Love to Read*

- ☐ ball mason cap
- ☐ balloon
- ☐ botany paper
- ☐ boxes
- ☐ branches
- ☐ butcher paper
- ☐ butter knife
- ☐ camera
- ☐ candy box
- ☐ cereal box
- ☐ cigar box
- ☐ clay
- ☐ colored paper
- ☐ construction paper
- ☐ computer
- ☐ crayons
- ☐ drawing paper
- ☐ dried beans
- ☐ exacto knife
- ☐ fabric scraps
- ☐ felt squares
- ☐ food coloring
- ☐ forms from *I Love to Read*
- ☐ gel icing
- ☐ gift box
- ☐ glitter

- ☐ glue
- ☐ hanger
- ☐ hole punch
- ☐ index cards
- ☐ magnet strip
- ☐ markers
- ☐ masking tape
- ☐ milk cartons
- ☐ odds and ends
- ☐ oven
- ☐ paintbrush
- ☐ papier-mache
- ☐ paper cup
- ☐ paper scraps
- ☐ paper towel tubes
- ☐ paste
- ☐ plain paper
- ☐ plastic detergent bottle
- ☐ plastic sewing needle
- ☐ pencil(s)
- ☐ pen(s)
- ☐ printer
- ☐ recipes
- ☐ ruler
- ☐ salt
- ☐ sand

- ☐ safety scissors
- ☐ scissors
- ☐ shelf paper
- ☐ shoe box
- ☐ soft sponges
- ☐ spray bottles
- ☐ square sheet of white paper
- ☐ stapler
- ☐ stones
- ☐ string
- ☐ tagboard
- ☐ tape
- ☐ tempera paint
- ☐ thread
- ☐ tissue paper
- ☐ wallpaper
- ☐ water
- ☐ yarn
- ☐ _____
- ☐ _____
- ☐ _____
- ☐ _____
- ☐ _____
- ☐ _____
- ☐ _____
- ☐ _____
- ☐ _____

Name:_____

Date: _____

Select one of the following book projects to share with your class:

Character Projects

- ❑ Sponge Character
- ❑ Talking Character
- ❑ Character Sculpture
- ❑ Bean Bag Character
- ❑ Cookie Characters
- ❑ Story Flip Book
- ❑ Character Accordion Book
- ❑ Character Magnets
- ❑ Character Trait Box
- ❑ Thumbprint Characters
- ❑ Pop-Up Dialogue
- ❑ Biography Monologue
- ❑ Character Mask
- ❑ Meet the Characters Book
- ❑ _____
- ❑ _____
- ❑ _____

Setting Projects

- ❑ Story Stones
- ❑ Triorama
- ❑ Setting Map
- ❑ Simple Diorama
- ❑ Sculpted Diorama
- ❑ Shoebox Story Scene
- ❑ Magnetic Story Frame
- ❑ Story Props
- ❑ Magnetic Story Map
- ❑ Literature Postcards
- ❑ Story Snow Scene
- ❑ Story Neighborhood
- ❑ Reader's Theater Scenery
- ❑ Storyboard
- ❑ _____
- ❑ _____
- ❑ _____

Plot Projects

- ❑ Beg., Middle, End Book
- ❑ Story Time Capsule
- ❑ Story Pop-Out
- ❑ Fold-a-Story
- ❑ Story Cube Pop-Up
- ❑ Story Retell
- ❑ Cereal Box Theater
- ❑ Story Newsletter
- ❑ Candy Box Retell
- ❑ First-Person Journal
- ❑ Non-Fiction Shape Book
- ❑ Story Banner
- ❑ Guess the Character
- ❑ Story Box
- ❑ _____
- ❑ _____
- ❑ _____

Chapter 3

Character Projects

Character

Characters can be like me and you. Or very, very different than we are too.

Sponge Character

page 36

Talking Character

page 38

Character Sculpture

page 40

Bean Bag Character

page 42

Cookie Characters

page 44

Story Flip Book

page 46

Character Accordion Book

page 48

Projects

Character Magnets

page 50

Character Trait Box

page 52

Thumbprint Characters

page 54

Pop-Up Dialogue

page 56

Biography Monologue

page 58

Character Mask

page 60

Meet the Characters Book

page 62

Authors decide who the characters will be. They create story characters for us to see.

Sponge Character

The sponge character can be used with the cereal box theater on page 112 to create a story play. Younger children really enjoy this project. Adult help may be required with cutting.

Materials:

Soft sponges (2)	Scissors
Pencil and paper cup	Glue
Googly eyes and yarn	Fabric paint

Goal:

To create a sponge puppet character which will be used in story retellings

Steps:

1. Select a story character. Using a paper cup, trace a circle on a sponge and cut it out.
2. Draw lines on the sponge (see directions).
3. Cut the top and bottom lines partly through the sponge to help you grab onto it.
4. Cut through the middle line to form a mouth.
5. Cut ears, nose, hair and other items out of the other sponge and yarn.
6. Glue eyes and other pieces on the face.
7. Put your fingers in the sponge back and talk for the character.

Sponge Character Directions

Steps 1 and 2

Select the character you want to use. Draw a circle on a sponge using a paper cup.

Step 3

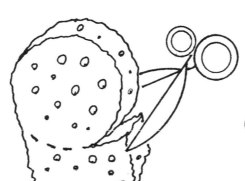

Cut the circle out.

Steps 4 and 5

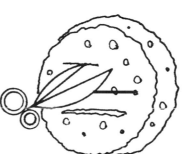

Draw three lines on the sponge. Cut the top and bottom lines partly through.

Step 6

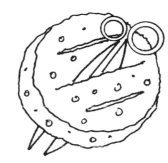

Cut the middle line all the way through to create a mouth.

Step 7

Cut ears, nose, hair, and other items out of the other sponge and yarn.

Step 8

Glue eyes and other pieces on the face.

Sample

Put your fingers in the back and talk for the character.

Talking Character

Creating a talking character is so much fun it naturally inspires children to write dialogue.

Materials:

Construction paper (12 x 9")
White paper (81/2" x 7")   Glue
Paper scraps/wallpaper   Scissors
Pencil/pens/markers

Goals:

To start writing dialogue
To predict what a character might say

Steps:

1. Fold construction and white paper in half.
2. Cut a 2" line in the center of the white paper fold line.
3. Fold the cut flaps back to form triangles.
4. Open the page and gently push the flaps back to create a V-shape (see directions).
5. Draw the character's face around the mouth. Make a dialogue bubble out of paper scraps. Write words the character might say inside it.

Talking Character Directions

Step 1

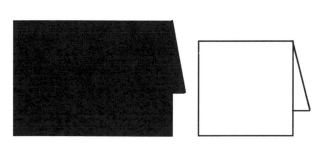

Fold construction paper (12" x 9").
Fold white paper (8 1/2" x 7").

Step 2

Measure and cut a 2 inch line
in the center of the fold of
the sheet of white paper.

Step 3

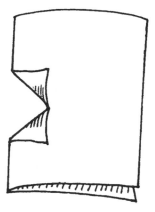

Form two triangle shapes by
folding each cut flap back.

Step 4

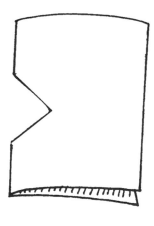

Open up the page and gently
push the flaps back inside to
form a V-shape.

Step 5

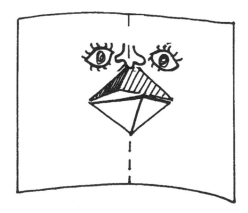

Draw the character's face around the
mouth by drawing and pasting
features on the page.

Sample

Create a dialogue bubble out of
paper scraps. Write words the
character would say inside.

Character Sculpture

This project is great for all ages and recycles many different materials. Character sculptures can become the main focus of a story retelling.

Materials:

Plastic detergent bottle   Scissors

Masking tape and glue   Newspapers

Sand (2 cups)   Tempera paint

Material scraps, buttons, yarn etc.

Papier-mache recipe (page 134)

Goal:

To create a sculpture of a story character

Steps:

1. Remove the cap and pour sand into bottle.
2. Wad a half sheet of newspaper into a ball.
3. Place ball in middle of the other half sheet.
4. Twist sheet around ball, place into the bottle's neck and tape to form a head.
5. Cut newspaper into strips and dip them into a papier-mache paste. Form a single layer of strips over the bottle and head.
6. Repeat the fifth step three more times, creating arms, legs or dress with new strips.
7. Paint your character and add any details.

Character Sculpture Directions

Step 1

Pour sand into bottle to keep it stable as you create your character sculpture.

Steps 2 and 3

Tear a piece of newspaper in half. Wad half the sheet into a ball. Place ball in the middle of the other half sheet and twist around to form a head.

Step 4

Place head into the top of the bottle and tape it.

Step 5

Cut newspaper into strips and dip them into a papier-mache paste. Form single layer of strips over bottle and head.

Step 6

Repeat the fifth step three more times, creating arms, legs or a dress with new strips.

Step 7

Paint character and add details with scraps of material, etc.

Bean Bag Character

Character bean bags are fun to make and become a story souvenir for years. Adult supervision may be required with younger children for sewing and cutting.

Materials:

Felt squares (2)   Drawing paper
Scissors   Pencil/markers
Glue   Googly eyes
Thread/needle   Dried beans
Yarn   Felt scraps

Goal:

To make a bean bag of your favorite character

Steps:

1. Draw the character's face on paper.
2. Cut two identical circles out of felt.
3. Cut nose and mouth out of scraps.
4. Glue eyes and face pieces on front circle.
5. Put front circle on top of back circle.
6. Sew shut all but an inch of the circle.
7. Fill opening half way full of dried beans and sew it shut.
8. Glue on yarn or other materials for hair.
9. Share your bean bag with your friends.

Bean Bag Character Directions

Step 1

Draw the character's
face on paper.

Step 2

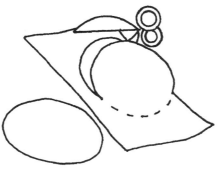

Cut two identical circles
out of felt.

Step 3

Cut nose and mouth
out of scraps.

Step 4

Glue eyes and face
pieces on front circle.

Steps 5 and 6

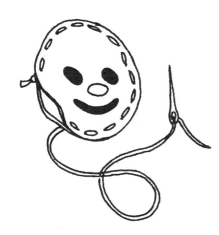

Put front circle on top of back circle.
Sew shut all but an inch of the circle.

Step 7

Fill opening half way full
of dried beans and sew shut.

Step 8

Glue on yarn or other materials for hair.

Cookie Characters

What could be more fun than creating cookie characters and then eating them? Children of all ages love this project.

Materials:

Cardboard	Pencil/scissors
Oven/pan/butter knife	Gel icing
Cookie recipe (page 133)	Scissors

Goal:

To bake story character cookies for a book celebration

Steps:

1. Draw one or more characters on a piece of cardboard. Cut out each character.
2. Make the sugar cookie recipe on page 133.
3. Roll dough on lightly floured pastry cloth.
4. Place cardboard character on the dough.
5. Use butter knife to cut around each character. Remove the cardboard.
6. Place each character on a lightly greased baking sheet. Bake at 400 degrees for 10 minutes or until they are light brown.
7. Place cookies on a rack to cool.
8. Decorate each cookie character.

Cookie Character Directions

Step 1

Draw one or more characters on a piece of cardboard. Cut out each character.

Step 2

Make sugar cookie recipe on page 133.

Step 3

Roll dough on lightly floured pastry cloth.

Steps 4 and 5

Place cardboard character on top of the dough and cut around it. Remove the cardboard.

Step 6

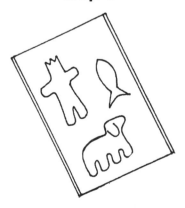

Place cookies on a lightly greased baking sheet. Bake at 400 degrees for 10 minutes.

Steps 7 and 8

Cool cookies on a rack. Decorate each character cookie with gel icing or tube frosting Eat the cookies during a book celebration.

Story Flip Book

The flip book is a project idea from Julee Neupert's classroom at Ben Rush Elementary in Redmond, WA. It could easily be adapted to become a plot or setting project.

Materials:

3 pieces of paper   Hole punch
Markers/pencils   Yarn

Goal:

To show how a character grows and changes in a story

Steps:

1. Fold: sheet #1 at 3", sheet #2 at 4" and sheet #3 at 5".
2. Place #1 over #2 ,#2 over #3, to make 6 pages.
3. Punch two holes at top and tie with yarn. Write the character's name on the top page.
4. Draw a picture of the character early in the story and write a description on page 2.
5. On pages 3, 4 and 5, draw events important to the character. Describe each in a sentence.
6. On page 6, draw a picture of the character at the end of the story and write a description
7. Share your flip book with your friends.

Story Flip Book Directions

Steps 1 and 2

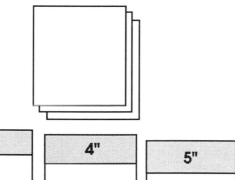

3"	4"	5"
1	2	3

Fold sheet 1 at 3" – sheet 2 at 4" – sheet 3 at 5"

Place sheet 1 over 2 and sheet 2 over 3 to create 6 pages.

Step 3

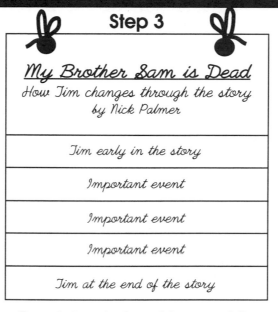

My Brother Sam is Dead
How Tim changes through the story
by Nick Palmer

Tim early in the story

Important event

Important event

Important event

Tim at the end of the story

Punch two holes at top and tie with yarn. Fill in the top page.

Step 4 (page 2)

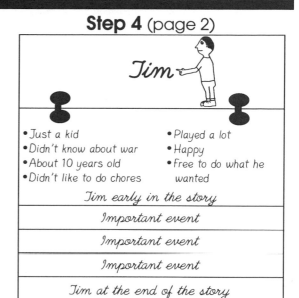

Tim

- Just a kid
- Didn't know about war
- About 10 years old
- Didn't like to do chores

- Played a lot
- Happy
- free to do what he wanted

Tim early in the story

Important event

Important event

Important event

Tim at the end of the story

Draw the character early in the story and write a description.

Step 5 (pages 3, 4, 5)

Tim and his father took their cattle to Fairfield Pt. They sold them for tavern supplies. On the way back Tim's father was kidnapped and Tim had to talk his way to safety when he was held up by cowboys.

Important event

Important event

Important event

Tim at the end of the story

Draw and describe an important story event on each page.

Step 6 (page 6)

Tim

- More grown-up
- Hated war
- About 13 years old
- Did all the farm chores

- Had responsibilities
- Sad because his dad, brother and friend died

Tim at the end of the story

Draw the character at the end of the story and write a description.

Character Accordion Book

The character accordion book is a simple and clear way to introduce young children to story characters.

Materials:

Tagboard   Scissors/tape
Accordion book (page 137)

Goal:

To create a special book with drawings of
 your favorite story characters

Steps:

1. Create an accordion book using the directions on page 137.
2. Think about the characters in the story.
3. Decide which characters you want to include in your book. Draw your favorite character on the front cover.
4 Draw a character on each page. Write in each character's name if you choose.
5. Draw the back cover of your book.
6. Share the book with your friends.

Character Accordion Book Example

Sister Bear

Papa Bear

Brother Bear

Mama Bear

This project was based on *The Berenstain Bears' New Neighbors,* by Stan and Jan Berenstain

Character accordion book created by Hannah Gibbons

Character Magnets

The students in Martha Ivy's and Valerie Marshall's classroom at McAuliffe Elementary in Redmond, WA, created magnets to fit on their magnetic story maps (page 84).

Materials:
Magnetic strips   Paint and varnish
Paintbrush
Baker's clay recipe (page 132)

Goal:
To create magnets of your favorite characters

Steps:
1. Decide which story characters you want to make.
2. Make the baker's clay recipe on page 132.
3. Mold the clay to look like the characters.
4. Place character paper on top of the dough.
5. Follow the recipe directions.
6. Place characters on a rack to cool.
7. When completely cool, paint each character.
8. When the character magnets are dry, spray the front with varnish.
9. Later, stick the magnetic strip on the back of the characters.

Character Magnet Examples

Babe Ruth
from
Babe Ruth
created by
Terry Yoo

Bilbo Baggins
and
Smaug
from
The Hobbit
created by
Nick Palmer

Sylvester Coddmyer, III
from
The Kid Who Only Hit Homers
created by
Steven Yoo

Character Trait Box

The character trait box was recommended by the students in Joyce Standing's class at The Overlake School in Redmond, WA. They suggest using fabric covered shelf paper to get a more textured look.

Materials:

Square box   Shelf paper (fabric)
Scissors   Pencil/markers
Glue   Construction paper

Goals:

To identify main and supporting characters
To list the traits of each story character

Steps:

1. Cover each side of the box with shelf paper.
2. Draw pictures of five characters on construction paper.
3. Think about each of the five characters. What are they like?
4. List a number of character traits for each character on strips of construction paper.
5. Glue characters and their traits on the box.
6. Share your character trait box with friends.

Character Trait Box Example

Mom

Polite

Organized

Hard Working

Affectionate

Imaginative

Claudia

Nice

Proper

Organized

Jamie Kincaid

Caring

Selfish

Smart

Thankful

This project was based on *The Mixed Up Files of Mrs. B. Frankweiler*
Character trait box created by Jamie Weaver

Thumbprint Characters

Julee Neupert's thumbprint characters idea is fun and allows her students to practice writing simple conversations between characters. The dialogue created can be used later in a reader's theater. A group discussion regarding dialogue is a great way to start this activity.

Materials:
Construction paper (18" x 12")
Pencil and black fine-tip pen
Ink pad (different colored pads are fun)

Goal:
To practice writing dialogue

Steps:
1. Select two or more story characters.
2. Think of things they might say to each other.
3. Divide the construction paper (18" x 12") into four equal sections.
4. Using an ink pad, make two thumbprints in each of the four sections. Draw arms and legs attached to each thumbprint.
5. Write what you think the characters would say to each other in dialogue bubbles.
6. Share your character conversations with friends.

Thumbprint Characters Example

This project was based on *Charlotte's Web* by E.B. White

Pop-Up Dialogue

The students in Ann Lyman's classroom at Westhill Elementary in Bothell, WA, find writing basic dialogue using this fun pop-up project a truly creative experience.

Materials:
Construction paper: (17" x 12")- sheet 1 and (12" x 9")- sheet 2
Colored/white paper   Glue
Markers/pencils   Scissors

Goals:
To write simple dialogue
To create a story scene with characters

Steps:
1. Decide how many pop-ups you want in your project. Fold sheets 1 and 2 in half. Open 2 and draw story scene on top quarter of page.
2. Use white paper to draw and cut out pop-ups.
3. Fold sheet 2 with the setting inside. Cut as many 2" tabs as you need for the pop-ups.
4. Open up and gently push cut tabs inside.
5. Center and glue sheet 2 to sheet 1.
6. Open up and glue pop-ups to the tabs you've created. On the base, write what you think characters would say.

Pop-Up Dialogue Directions

Step 1

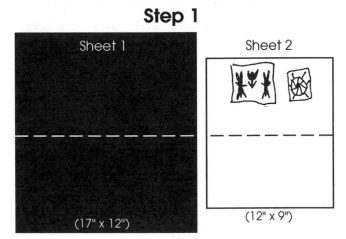

Sheet 1

(17" x 12")

Sheet 2

(12" x 9")

Fold sheet 1 and sheet 2 in half. Open sheet 2 and draw scene on top quarter of page.

Step 2

Draw and cut out pop-ups.

Step 3

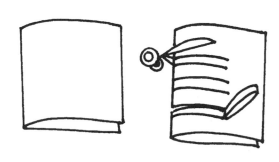

Fold sheet 2 with the scene illustration inside. Cut as many 2" tabs as you need for the pop-ups.

Step 4

Open up and gently push cut tabs inside.

Step 5

Center and glue sheet 2 to sheet 1 (don't glue tabs down).

Step 6

Open up and glue pop-ups to tabs. Write dialogue on the base.

Sample

And Ms. Rooney's room wins the Blue Banner! Said Mr. Mancina! Yeah!

Biography Monologue

The students in Nancy Johnston's class at Wilder Elementary in Redmond, WA, thoroughly enjoyed becoming a character from a biography. They dressed up as the character and used their monologue sheets or notecards to give a presentation to the class.

Materials:

Index cards   Paper

Costume (you create)   Pencil/markers

Goal:

To present a monologue as if you were the person in the biography

Steps:

1. Select the person you want to be. Imagine that you are the person.
2. On notecards write:
   - An introduction of yourself (as the character)
   - Something meaningful or significant in your life
   - What your dreams were
   - What your motivation was
   - People important to your personal development
   - Why the biography was written
   - Advice you would give to others
3. Write your notes on paper if you like.
4. Dress up as the character and share the monologue with your friends.

Biography Monologue Examples

Monologue Sheet

Page 1
Cochise
by Willie Nelson

I am Cochise, leader of a band of Apache. I was born high in the Dos Cabeza Mountains in eighteen hundred and five. I was taught to hunt at the age of nine by my father. I learned how to survive and live off of the land. As a test, I was left on my own for seven days.

At the age of eleven I was allowed to go on my first hunting trip. I learned to contribute however I could. In time, I became a great hunter capable of leading my people.

My father died and I became Chief at the age of thirty-six. I carried out my father's wish to keep peace with the white for the next twenty three years without conflict.

A mistake by the white eyes led to war. The white eyes thought the Apache had stolen a young whiteboy. I came with several other Apache to see the white eyes, bearing the white flags of peace. We offered to help find the boy who had run away. The white eyes had tricked us and attempted to ambush us. The events that followed are now known as the Cut The Tent Affair. I escaped by slitting the tent and escaping out the back. Many of my relatives were not so lucky. I pledged to avenge their deaths which lead to twenty years of war against the white eyes.

We made peace with the white eyes two years before my death. Only 128 of the 558 Warriors lived to see peace.

I died on June 7th, 1874. I was buried in a sacred Indian burial ground for the Apache chiefs now known as Indian Gorge. I was dressed as a warrior and laid to rest with my horse and dog.

The advice I would share with the youth is that peace and happiness is everything. You take it for granted until it's gone. But what is even more important is to believe in yourself. There are no limits to what you can do.

What motivated me was that because I was the chief, I would have to do the best thing for my people and forget my personal wants. Even if it meant going to war or living on a reservation.

The childhood events and dreams that helped me accomplish all that I did were first, that I wanted to be a great chief and become a great warrior who would be feared by all. I accomplished these things but it wasn't easy.

My life was full of wars, pain, blood and especially tears. In war I had to watch my people die. I lived in pain when my family members were hung.

A biography was written about me because I was an important Apache chief and I was know for terrorizing the white eyes for many years.

The person who helped me most during my life was my father. As an Apache chief he taught me the ways of our people. He also taught me to survive and to preserve the ways of our people.

Monologue Note Cards

(1)
Introduction
by Greg Lundwall

Hi! I'm Chuck Yeager from the United States Air Force. I was born on February 13, 1923, in West Virginia. I was fifteen when I saw my first airplane. After that day I had always dreamed of flying one day. When I turned nineteen

(3)   Meaningful or Significant

Something meaninful or significant in my life was breaking the Sound Barrier in 1947. The Sound Barrier is an invisible wall that forms at 1,129 feet per second, also known as Mach 1. I broke that barrier in Muroc Airbase in California's

(6)
Motivation

In my younger years my mom and dad motivated me to what I am today. They told me to try my best. When I grew up and got married I was motivated by my wife Glennis and my kids. I was also motivated by my flight instructor.

Character Mask

Julee Neupert's students make character masks. They find masks to be great props for a story retellings.

Materials:
Papier-mache recipe (page 134)
Tempera paint/brushes   Scissors
9 inch balloon

Goal:
To create a character mask

Steps:
1. Blow up a 9" balloon to the size of a head.
2. Make the papier-mache recipe on page 134.
3. Tear newspaper into 3" strips. Dip strips into papier-mache recipe. Cover only half of the balloon with strips. Repeat three times.
4. Twist newspaper to make eyebrows, nose and lips. Cover with papier-mache strips.
5. Add top layer of dry strips creating a smooth surface. Turn mask over every day for 7 days.
6. At the end of the 7 days, if the mask is dry pop the balloon and trim the edges.
7. Paint mask and use it to retell the story.

Character Mask Directions

Step 1

Blow up a 9 inch balloon to the size of a head.

Steps 2 and 3

Make the papier-mache recipe on page 134. Tear newspaper into 3" strips and dip into mixture. Cover half of the balloon with strips. Repeat three times.

Step 4

Twist newspaper to create eyebrows, nose and lips. Cover each with strips.

Step 5

Add top layer of dry strips, creating a smooth surface. Let the mask dry for 7 days. Turn it over every day.

Step 6

When completely dry, pop the balloon and trim the edges of the mask.

Sample

Paint the character mask and use it in a retelling of the story.

Meet the Characters Book

Joyce Standing's students found their Meet the Characters books provided an opportunity to reveal interesting story information through character descriptions.

Materials:
Book recipes (pages 136-139
Pencil/pen/markers

Goal:
To create a book in which various story characters are introduced

Steps:
1. Determine the type of book you want to make from the book recipes (pages 136-139).
2. Select the characters you want to include in your book.
3. Design and create your book cover.
4. Make the title page (see example).
5. Write about the characters on the left-hand pages and draw the characters on the right.
6. Create a comments page on which your friends will write what they like about the book.
7. Share your book with friends.

Meet the Characters Book Example

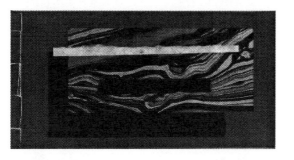

Martin

When Martin was a young mouse his father, Luke the Warrior, had to go to Salaman-dastron to fight. He said if he didn't return by fall that Martin should wander off to a differernt land. Martin waited till the end of fall. Luke still hadn't returned. So he set off on his journey.

After awhile he found his way to Mossflower. After wandering around for awhile Martin was captured by the Kotir warriors and taken to the evil queen Tsarmina's dirty cells. He was only there for a bit because a stranger named Gonff the Mousethief was put in the same cell. Little did Martin know that Gonff could pick any lock in all of Moss-

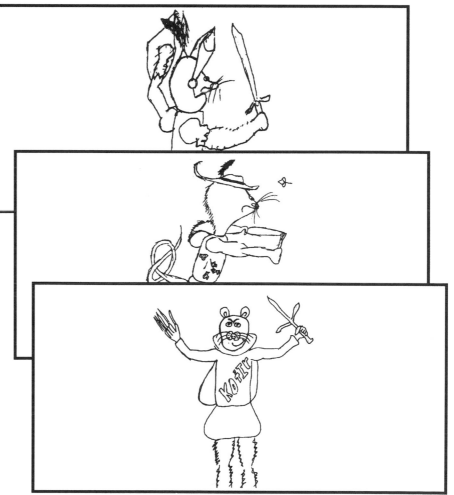

Gonff

Gonff was a jolly little mousethief who was happy all the time. One day while he was humming his way through mossflower he was captured. Gonff didn't really care. He knew how to pick locks, so he wouldn't be in any cell for long. Once he fot to the cells, he was thrown in with a young warrior mouse named Martin. When Gonff decided to get himself out of the cell, he got his new friend Martin out too.

After that they went through every battle and adventure together. When Matin had to go to Salmandastron he chose his best friend, Gonff, and a young strong mole named Dinney to go with him. They ran into a lot of problems, but made it all in one piece. They found Boar the Fighter at a bad time because Ripfang, the sea rat, was

Tsarmina

Tsarmina was a wildcat who had an evil mind and desperately wanted to become ruler of Kotir. So she killed her father, the ruler of Kotir, and she became the ruler. She had no mercy and was determined to defeat Mossflower. Day and night she would be thinking of a way to capture the animals of Mossflower. One day she succeeded by capturing two of the bravest mice in all of Mossflower, Martin and Gonff. But they escaped.

One day while she was out in the battlefields a young fox and his group met her and they became a strong team. Bane the Fox had an evil mind, too. Bane and Tsarmina came up with great battle plans, but still they couldn't overcome Mossflower. One day Tsarmina's trust of Bane began t fade, and they got in a fight. While Bane was out in the battlefields a hawk swooped down on him and killed him. Then she realized that the Mossflower warriors' plan to flood her castle, Kotir, was working. Next, a boulder hit Kotir and cracked it. After three more boulders hit, Kotir had fallen. Tsarmina hopped on a table and floated down the Mossflower River. When she met up with Martin they fought a brutal fight and then she drowned in the Mossflower River.

My Character Project Supply Sheet

Name:

My Project is:_____

To do my project I will need:

___ Recipe:_____
    page #

Writing Tools

___ pencil(s)
___ pen(s)
___ marker(s)
___ crayons
___ ruler

Art Supplies

___ glue
___ scissors
___ felt squares
___ fabric paint
___ ribbon
___ paint
___ paint brush
___ tempera paint
___ glitter
___ dried beans
___ googly eyes
___ exacto knife
___ odds and ends

Paper Supplies

___ form: page #
___ plain paper
___ construction paper
___ butcher paper
___ tagboard
___ cardboard
___ cardboard box
___ contact paper
___ colored paper

Other Possible Items

___ book
___ ink pad
___ paper cup
___ scotch/masking tape
___ paper scraps
___ sponge(s)
___ pan
___ balloon
___ butter knife
___ hole punch
___ plastic sewing needle
___ yarn/cord
___ newspaper
___ sand
___ plastic detergent bottle
___ oven
___ costume

Chapter 4

Setting Projects

Setting

The Setting tells us when and where, so we can feel as if we were really there.

Story Stones

page 68

Triorama

page 70

Setting Map

page 72

Simple Diorama

page 74

Sculpted Diorama

page 76

Shoebox Story Scene

page 78

Magnetic Story Frame

page 80

Projects

Story Props

The Story of the Missing Red Mitten

page 82

Magnetic Story Map

Woodland Park Zoo

page 84

Literature Postcards

page 86

Story Snow Scene

page 88

Story Neighborhood

page 90

Reader's Theater Scenery

page 92

Storyboard

page 94

The author paints a picture for you and me. Use your imagination and the setting you'll see!

Story Stones

Story stones can feature story characters or story scenes. Kids enjoy trading stones from their story collections.

Materials:

Stones (smooth)   Glue
Poster paints/markers   Paintbrush
Construction paper   Pencil
Yarn/fabric scraps

Goal:

To decorate a stone with the image of a story character or story scene

Steps:

1. Find four smooth stones from outside.
2. Decide which characters and scenes you want to draw on your stones.
3 Wash and dry each stone.
4. Draw your design on each stone in pencil.
5. Use paint or markers to fill in your design.
6. Glue on any extra items.
7. Share your story stones with friends.

Story Stone Examples

Story stone based on *In the Face of Danger*
Created by Brian Schnierer

Story stone based on *Meet Kirsten*
Created by Emily Gibbons

Story stone based on *Island of the Blue Dolphins*
Created by Tara O'Brien

Story stone based on *Shiloh*
Created by Terry Yoo

Triorama

The triorama comes highly recommended by students in Julee Neupert's classroom. This project is an amazingly simple and fun way to create a three-dimensional story scene.

Materials:
Square sheet of white paper (12" x 12")

Crayons/markers	Glue
Scissors	Colored paper
String	Tape

Goal:
To create a three-dimensional story scene

Steps:
1. Select a story scene for your triorama. Fold both sides of a square sheet of paper in half diagonally, creating four triangle panels.
2. Draw the scene in panels 1 and 2.
3. Draw the base of the scene on panel 3.
4. Cut between panel 3 and 4, then fold and glue panel 4 underneath panel 3.
5. Draw story characters and objects. Cut them out and glue them to the base.
6. Glue an object or character to a piece of string and hang it from the triorama point.

Triorama Directions

Step 1

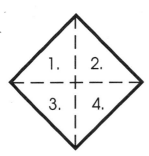

Fold both sides of 12" x 12" paper in half diagonally.

Step 2

Draw the scene in panels one and two.

Step 3

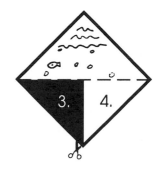

Draw the base of the scene on panel 3.

Step 4

Cut between panel 3 and 4, then fold and glue panel 4 underneath panel 3.

Step 5

Draw characters and story objects. Cut them out and glue them to the base.

Step 6

Glue an object and/or character to a piece of string and hang it from the triorama.

Sample

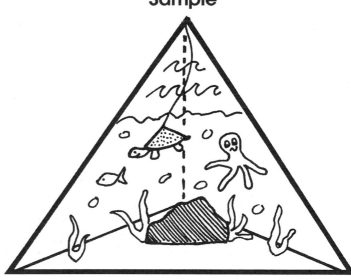

Share your finished triorama.

Setting Map

Ann Lyman's students enjoy drawing maps of how they imagine the main story setting would look. This is a great partner project.

Materials:
Butcher paper (23 1/2" x 18")   Markers/pens

Goal:
To draw a map of a story's main setting

Steps:
1. Close your eyes and think about the story. Imagine a map of the setting.
2. Write a list of places and things you want to include on your map.
3. Draw your map using this list to guide you.
4. Find a map of your city or state. Look at how it is folded.
5. Fold your map in half. Then fold it in fourths using the same kind of accordion fold used in a city map.
6. On an outside panel of the map write the title of the book, the setting and your name. Share your map with friends.

Setting Map Example

This setting map was based on *The Cay*

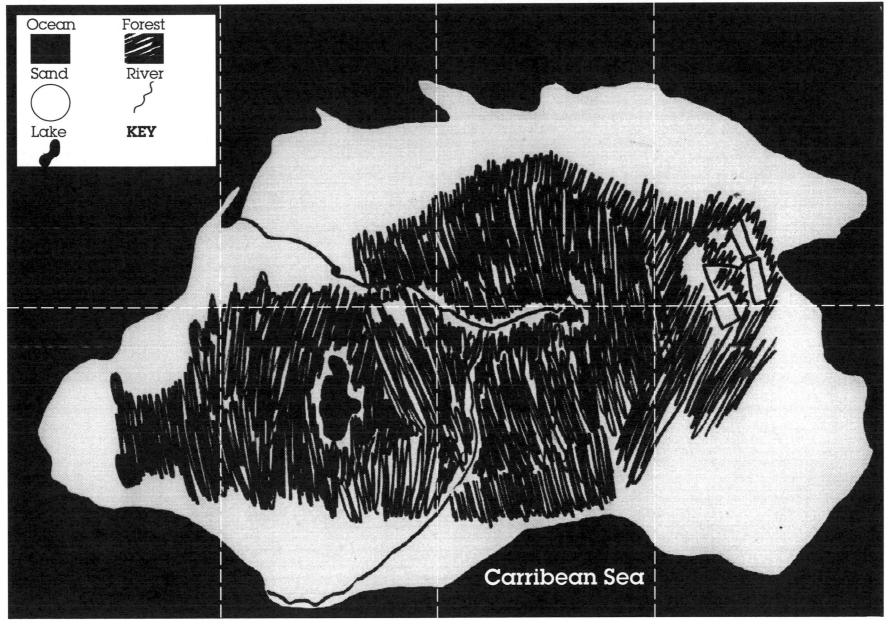

KEY
- Ocean
- Forest
- Sand
- River
- Lake

Carribean Sea

This project was created by Michael Strong and Chris Hartsell

Simple Diorama

This diorama is simple to make. Characters can be created with clay or requisitioned from the toy chest. It could easily be transformed into a book report by writing character and story information on the box top and sides.

Materials:

Gift box	Paper (all sorts)
Scissors	Tape
Glue	Markers

Odds and ends (rocks, branches, clay, toys)

Goal:

To create a story scene in a box

Steps:

1. Decide which story scene you want to use in your diorama.
2. Turn box on its side, placing the lid underneath (see example).
3. Create the scene from odds and ends you you find in a park or a toy chest.
4. Cover the box outside and/or inside with paper if you like.
5. Create characters out of clay or dolls.
6. Draw any other items you want to include.

Simple Diorama Example

Simple diorama based on *The Summer of My German Soldier*
Created by Carey DeAngelis

Sculpted Diorama

The sculpted diorama is especially fun to create. The sculpted back is like scenery on a stage. Adult supervision may be required for cutting.

My Diorama
for
Tuck Everlasting

Materials:

Shoebox	Paper (all sorts)
Scissors	Tape
Glue	Markers

Odds and ends (rocks, branches, clay)

Goal:

To create a story scene in a shoebox with a scenery-like back

Steps:

1. Decide which story scene you want to use in your diorama.
2. Remove the shoebox lid and turn box on its side. Cut off the top section of the box.
3. Cut sides at an angle as shown on next page.
4. Cut the back of the box to fit the scene.
5. Create a setting scene from odds and ends you find in a park or the yard.
6. Create characters out of clay or construction paper. Place or glue items inside box.
7. Draw any other items you want to include.

Sculpted Diorama Directions

Steps 1 and 2

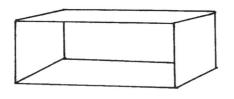

Remove shoe box lid, turn box on its side and cut off the top section.

Step 3

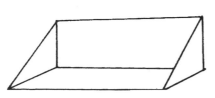

Cut sides at an angle.

Step 4

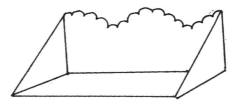

Cut the back of the box to fit the scene.

Step 5

Create setting scene from odds and ends.

Steps 6 and 7

Create characters out of clay or construction paper.
Draw any other items you want to include.
Place them inside the shoebox.

Sample

Share your sculpted diorama with friends.

Shoebox Story Scene

The students in Pam Schild's class at Wilder Elementary enjoy creating many different reading extension projects. The shoebox story scene was one of their favorite projects. Adult supervision may be required for cutting.

Materials:

Shoebox (with lid)   Markers
Scissors/exacto knife   Pencil/crayons
Construction paper   Glue/tape

Goal:

To create a story scene

Steps:

1. Decide which story scene you want to create. Cut a piece of construction paper to fit inside the bottom of a shoe box.
2. Create a 3-dimensional scene from the story on the construction paper.
3. Cover the box and lid with paper.
4. Cut a square (2") window in the center of one end of the lid.
5. Decorate the box with items from the story.
6. Cut a small peek hole in one end of the box.
7. Place the scene in the bottom of the box.

Shoebox Story Scene Directions

Step 1

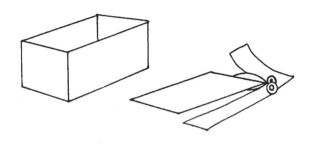

Cut a piece of construction paper to fit inside the bottom of the shoebox.

Step 2

Create a 3-dimensional scene from a story on the construction paper.

Step 3

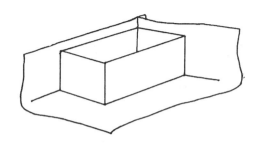

Cover the shoe box and lid with construction paper or shelf paper.

Step 4

Cut a two inch square window in the center of one end of the lid.

Step 5

Decorate the box with items from the story.

Step 6

Cut a small peek hole in one end of the box.

Step 7

Place the scene in the bottom of thebox and share it with your friends.

Magnetic Story Frame

The magnetic story frame is a great recycling project. Ball mason jars are used for storing homemade jams. They can be found in most grocery stores.

Materials:

Tagboard and paper   Scissors and glue
Pencil/markers   Tissue paper
Magnet strip (3")   Ball mason cap

Goal:

To create a magnetic story scene

Steps:

1. Use the rim of the cap's metal lid to trace two circles on tagboard and paper. Use the band's rim to trace a larger circle onto tagboard. Cut the three circles out.
2. Draw a story scene on the paper circle and glue it to the smaller tagboard circle.
3. Turn the band over and glue the story scene face down to its inside.
4. Place wadded tissue inside frame. Glue the larger tagboard circle to the frame edge.
5. Stick the magnetic strip to the tagboard.

Magnetic Story Frame Directions

Step 1

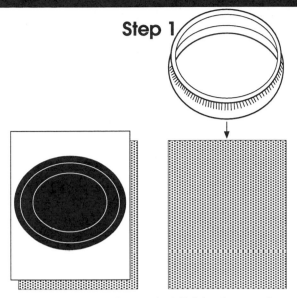

Use the rim of the cap's metal lid to trace two circles: paper and tagboard. Use the band's rim to trace a larger circle onto tagboard. Cut the circles out.

Step 2

Draw a story scene on the paper circle and glue it to the same sized tagboard circle.

Step 3

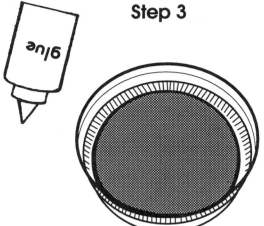

Turn the cap band over. Glue the circles face down to the inside of the band.

Sample
by Meghan Gibbons

Step 4

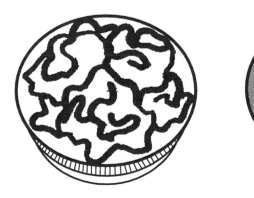

With the frame upside down, place wadded tissue inside the cap. Glue the larger tagboard circle to the outside edge of the cap's band.

Step 5

Stick the magnetic strip to the tagboard.

Turn your frame over and place it on your refrigerator.

Story Props

Story props complement any book-talk or book presentation. As shown on the next page, story props take many different forms. Imagination is the most important ingredient in this project.

Materials:

Tagboard	Paper
Scissors	Pencil/markers
Glue	Odds and ends
Clay	

Goal:

To create a story prop for use in a retelling

Steps:

1. List items which were very important to the story. Select two or three to use in your retelling.
2. Make the items with clay or other materials and attach them to a large piece of tagboard.
3. Write the book title and your name on the project.
4. Include any other items which will help retell the story.

Story Prop Examples

Metropolitan
Cafe
Sandwich
Grilled cheese sandwich	$1.95
Ham sandwich	$1.95
BLT	$1.95
Club sandwich	$1.95
Grilled chicken sandwich	$1.95

Snacks
Peanutbutter crackers	$ .50
Bubble gum lime, raspberry, grape	$ .25
Cereal	$ .45
Cookies Chocolate chip, oatmeal	$ .50
Chocolate Mousse cake	$2.00

Beverage
Juices	
Pineapple	$ .35
Apple	$ .35
Other	
Coffee	$ .25
Water	

From the Mixed—up Files of
Mrs. Basil E. Frankweiler

By Billy Harris & Eunice Chung

Magnetic Story Map

Valerie Marshall and Martha Ivy created the setting map on the right for their classroom magnetic board. The students in their classroom made character magnets (page 50) and attached them to the map as they followed it through the story.

Materials:

Large sheet of paper   Markers/pencils
Overhead projector   Tape
Magnetic writing board

Goal:

To create a story map for use on a magnetic board

Steps:

1. Draw a larger version of a map in a book by using an overhead projector.
2. Tape the map to a magnetic writing board.
3. As you and your classmates read through the story, place your character magnets at the appropriate setting location on the map.

Magnetic Story Map Example

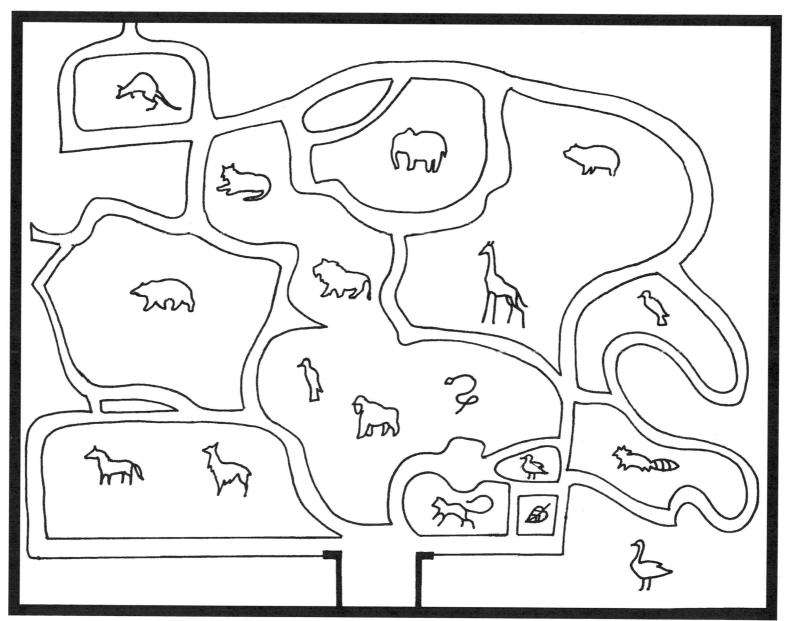

This magnetic story map was based on *Terror at the Zoo*

Literature Postcards

Writing a literature postcard to a pen pal is a unique way of sharing a reading experience. Kids enjoy corresponding with each other in words and pictures.

Materials:
Index card(s)   Stamp(s)

Pen/pencil/markers

Goal:
To discuss a story you are reading with a pen pal

Steps:
1. Find a book you and your pen pal both want to read.
2. Decide how many pages you'll read before the first postcard.
3. Decide which person will write first.
4. The first person sends a postcard with something they really like in the story. You can include writing and drawings.
5. The other person sends a postcard back saying how they like the book.
6. Continue sending postcards until you've finished reading the story.

Literature Postcard Examples

Nick Palmer
123 Bent Oak Dr.
Kirkland, WA
  98083

 STAMP

To: Tara Nichole O'Brien
  345 Berna Lane
  Newport Beach, CA
   90012

Tara Nichole O'Brien
345 Berna Lane
Newport Beach, CA
  90012

 STAMP

To: Nick Palmer
  123 Bent Oak Dr.
  Kirkland, WA
   98083

Hi Tara,   January 30, 1995
 I'm reading the book, *Island of the Blue Dolphins*, too. I really like it. My favorite character is Karama. I like her because she is really brave. I think she was very courageous when she jumped off the boat to get Ramo.
 I also think that Rontu was a good dog. I would like to have him as a pet. Who is your favorite character?
        Nick

Hi Nick,
 Karama is my favorite character too. Here is what I think she looks like.

Tara

Hi Tara,   February 12, 1995
 My favorite part of the book was when Karama got Rontu. That's when Rontu was the leader of the wild dogs and she was going to kill him but she wouldn't let herself do it. Then she ended up raising him and he liked her.
 What is your favorite part of the story so far?
 I like your drawing of Karama and the island.
        Nick

Hi Nick,
 My favorite part of the book so far is when Karama was gathering abalone. This is what I think it looked like.

Tara

Story Snow Scene

Molding a story snow scene is a great winter project. It is a unique and incredibly fun way to extend a literature experience.

Materials:

Spray bottles   Water

Snow   Food coloring

Camera   Paper/pencil

Goal:

To mold a three-dimensional story snow scene

Steps:

1. Select a scene from the story and draw it on a piece of paper.
2. Mold your scene in the snow (small houses, snow figures, buildings, etc).
3. Fill spray bottles with water and food coloring to create the colors you want to include in your snow scene.
4. Paint the scenery with the spray bottles.
5. Share your story snow scene with friends.
6. Take a picture of your snow scene before it melts.

Story Snow Scene Directions

Step 1

Select a scene from the story and draw it on a piece of paper.

Step 2

Mold your scene in the snow (small houses, snow figures, buildings, etc.)

Step 3

Fill spray bottles with food coloring and water to create the colors you want to include in your snow scene.

Sample

Paint the scenery with spray bottles and share your story snow scenes with friends. Don't forget to take a picture!

Story Neighborhood

Building a story neighborhood takes story comprehension and imagination. Kid's rate this as one of their favortie projects.

Materials:

Cartons/boxes   Construction paper
Scissors   Pencil/markers
Glue/tape/paste   Odds and ends

Goal:

To create a story neighborhood out of every-
   day materials

Steps:

1. Think about your favorite character's
   neighborhood in the story.
2. Draw a picture of what the neighborhood
   might look like. Collect project materials.
3. Cut a sheet of construction paper to fit
   around each carton and box.
4 Glue the paper to the cartons and boxes.
5. Create windows, doors and other items
   out of construction paper. Glue them to
   the milk carton and box buildings.
6. Draw any other items on the buildings.

Story Neighborhood Directions

Steps 1 and 2

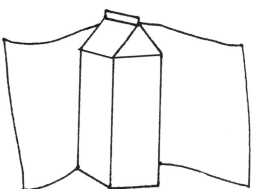

Draw a picture of what you think the story's neighborhood looks like.

Step 3

Cut a sheet of construction paper to fit around each carton and box.

Step 4

Glue the paper to the cartons or boxes.

Step 5

Create windows, doors etc., out of construction paper. Glue them to the new buildings.

Step 6

Draw any other items you want to include on the buildings.

Sample

Share your story neighborhood with your friends!

Reader's Theater Scenery

The reader's theater scenery is a perfect backdrop for a sponge character (page 36) story dramatization.

Materials:
Butcher paper   Markers/pencils
Paint   Paper
Paint brushes

Goal:
To create story scenery for a play

Steps:
1. Think about where the story takes place (setting) and imagine what it looks like.
2. Draw a picture of the setting on a piece of paper.
3. Get your materials ready and create your scenery.
4. Let the scenery dry, and then hang it up to use it in your play.

Reader's Theater Scenery Example

Scenery created by Edward Lobdell for the book, *Silver*

Storyboard

Storyboards are a very graphic tool in a presentation or retelling. Martha Ivy's and Valerie Marshall's students draw scenes from stories as they are read aloud. These scenes are then added to their classroom storyboard.

Materials:
Tagboard   Paper
Ruler   Pencil/markers
Glue

Goal:
To create a board that shows six or more scenes in a story

Steps:
1. List at least six important story events.
2. Think through what happened in the events. Draw a picture of each event.
3. Write a short sentence underneath each drawing explaining the scene.
4. Glue the scenes to a piece of tagboard and share your storyboard with friends.

Storyboard Example

Shiloh Story Board by Terry and Steven Yoo

Terry

1. Shiloh follows Marty home.

Steven

2. Shiloh was returned to it's owner.

Steven

3. Shiloh got attacked by German shephard.

Terry

4. Shiloh goes to the doctor.

Steven

5. Marty works fo[r] [J]udd Travers.

Terry

6. Marty gets to keep Shiloh

My Setting Project Supply Sheet

Name:

My Project is:_____

To do my project I will need:

___ Recipe:_____

page #

Writing Tools

___ pencil(s)
___ marker(s)
___ pen(s)
___ crayons
___ ruler

Art Supplies

___ glue
___ poster paint
___ scissors
___ paint
___ paintbrush
___ string
___ stickers
___ yarn
___ clay
___ exacto knife

Paper Supplies

___ form:page #
___ plain paper
___ lined paper
___ construction paper
___ cardstock paper
___ butcher paper
___ tagboard
___ cardboard
___ colored paper
___ contact paper
___ index card(s)

Other Possible Items

___ stones
___ shoebox
___ camera
___ milk cartons
___ ruler
___ magnet strip
___ gift box
___ magnetic board
___ food coloring
___ stamp(s)
___ spray bottle
___ odd boxes
___ ball mason cap
___ overhead projector
___ tissue paper

Chapter 5

Plot Projects

Plot

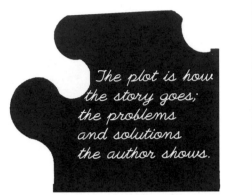

The plot is how the story goes; the problems and solutions the author shows.

Beginning, Middle and End Book

page 100

Story Time Capsule

page 102

Story Pop-Out

page 104

Fold-a-Story

Today's Fold-a-Story
Deep Trouble
by Franklin W. Dixon

Characters
Plot
Setting
Conflict

page 106

Story Cube Pop-Up

page 108

Story Retell Poster

Brian—Hatchet

page 110

Cereal Box Theater

page 112

Projects

Story Newsletter

page 114

Candy Box Retell

page 116

First-Person Journal

page 118

Non-Fiction Shape Book

page 120

Story Banner

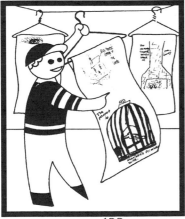

page 122

Guess the Character Book

page 124

Story Box

page 126

Stories can surprise you as they twist and turn, teaching us lessons the characters learn.

Beginning, Middle and End Book

The beginning, middle and end book is a fun introduction to plot for younger children. The written information can be dictated.

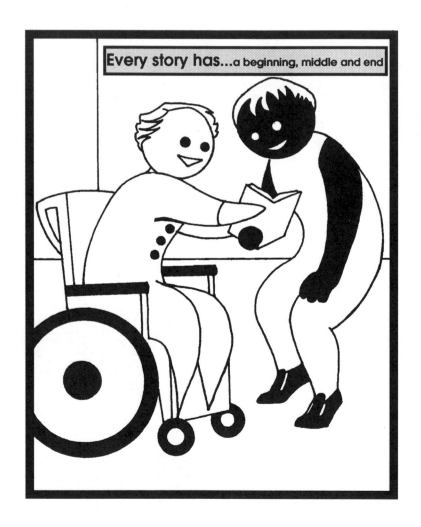

Every story has...a beginning, middle and end

Materials:
Pencil(s)/markers
Card book recipe (page 136)
Form (copy – page 148)

Goal:
To identify a story's beginning, middle and end

Steps:
1. Copy the form on page 148. Follow the directions for the card book on page 136.
2. Draw a picture of your favorite character on the front cover.
3. On the first page of your book, draw what happened in the beginning of the story.
4. On the next page, draw what happened in the middle of the story.
5. On the last page, draw what happened in the end of the story.

Beginning, Middle and End Book Example

My Beginning, Middle, and End Book

My Favorite Character

Story: _Dance at Grandpas_
My name: Justin Lobdell

Book Cover

This happened in the **beginning**...

In the beginning baby Carie and her sister and her mom and dad are going to their grandpas on a a horse pulling a sled.

First Page

This happened in the **middle**...

In the middle, their grandpa was changing all the babies diapers.

Second Page

This happened in the **end**...

At the very, very end, everybody at Grandpa's house is dancing.

Back Page

Story Time Capsule

The students in Nancie Schonhard's classroom at Wilder Elementary had a wonderful time creating unique time capsules for the books they were reading. Three of their projects are shown on the next page. This is a very open ended project.

Materials:

Recycled items   Markers/pens

Paint   Glue

Goal:

To create a time capsule for a story

Steps:

1. Close your eyes and imagine you were one of the story characters.
2. Write a list of items you would include in a time capsule which would tell others about your life as this character.
3. Decide upon the actual form of the time capsule (see examples). Make sure it relates to the story in some way.
4. Collect items you will need for the inside.
5. Make your time capsule and place the story items inside.
6. Share your time capsule with friends.

Story Time Capsule Examples

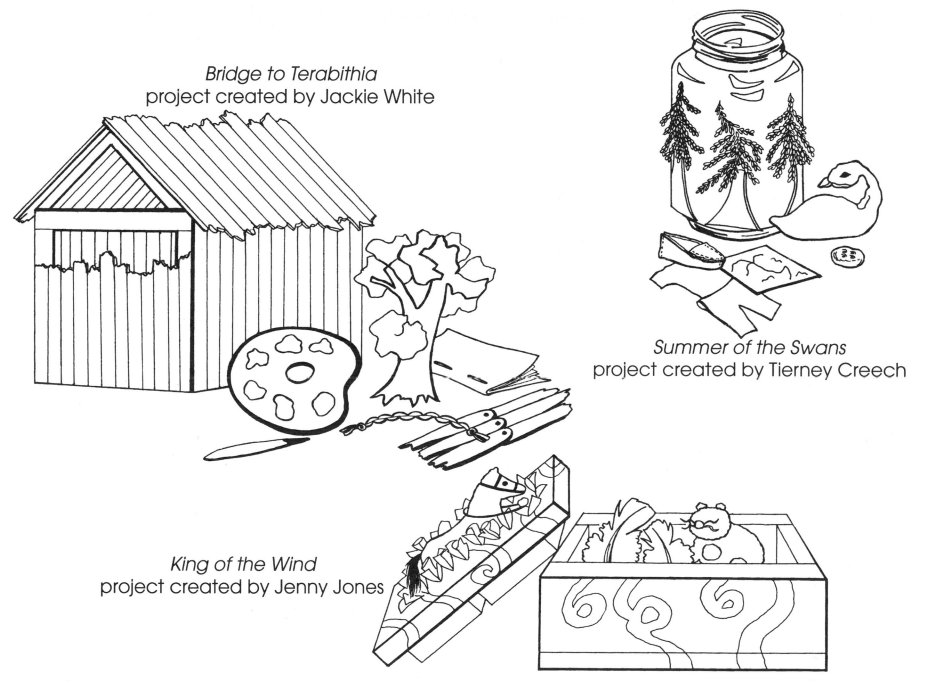

Bridge to Terabithia
project created by Jackie White

Summer of the Swans
project created by Tierney Creech

King of the Wind
project created by Jenny Jones

Story Pop-Out

Materials:
Construction paper (18" x 12")

Scissors   Pencil/crayons

Glue

Goal:
To create a house from a story and use it to retell the story

Steps:
1. Fold two sides of a sheet of construction paper into the middle.
2. Cut the top in a roof shape (see example).
3. Draw a character and write the title, author and your name on the cover.
4. Cut a large door and two windows out of construction paper scraps. Glue them to the inside of the house shape.
5. Write the story summary and character information on inside panels.
6. Draw characters in the windows and door.

Story Pop-Out Directions

Steps 1 and 2

(18" x 12")

Fold two sides of construction paper into the middle.
Cut each side at an angle to form a peak.

Step 3

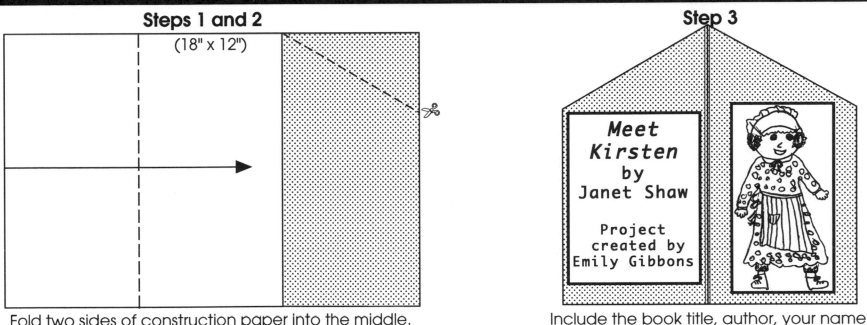

Meet Kirsten
by
Janet Shaw

Project
created by
Emily Gibbons

Include the book title, author, your name
and a picture of the character.

Step 4
Cut a large door and two windows
out of construction paper. Glue to
the inside of the house shape.

Step 5
Write the story summary and
information about your favorite
character on inside panels.

Step 6
Draw characters in the
windows and door.

Story Summary
Kirsten was from Sweden. Her family traveled on a boat to get to America. Her friend, Marta, was with them and she died from a fever on the boat.

When Kirsten got to America she was following her dad and her brother, Peter to get some milk and she got lost. She was very scared. A nice lady found her and took her back.

Then she lived with her cousins, Anna and Lisbeth. She thought they were very kind and liked playing with them.

Anna Olav

Lisbeth Olav

Kirsten

Story Characters
The main character in this story is Kirsten. Kirsten is Swedish. She's a Viking. She is nice. She has blonde hair. She wears her hair in braids looped up. She is 9 years old and she lives with her cousins.

Another character is Anna. She's Kirsten's cousin. She has blonde hair too, but she was born in America. She is nice to Kirsten.

Lisbeth is Anna's sister. She has brownish hair. She's older than Kirsten. She acts more grown up than Kirsten and Anna.

Fold-a-Story

The fold-a-story is open ended, easy to make and can be adjusted for all ages. Nancy Johnston's students at Wilder Elementary find it to be a great presentation tool or book report.

Materials:
A square piece of construction paper
Pencil/pens/markers

Goal:
To identify key elements in a story

Steps:
1. Fold construction paper in half to create two triangles.
2. Fold top and bottom corners to the center.
3. Fold remaining sides to form a square.
4. Write story information on the four sides. The project front can include your name, the date, book title with author and other interesting information.
5. The inside can include a scene drawn in the square, and information on setting, plot, characters and main conflict in each flap.
6. Pop open your square to reveal the story.

Fold-a-Story Directions

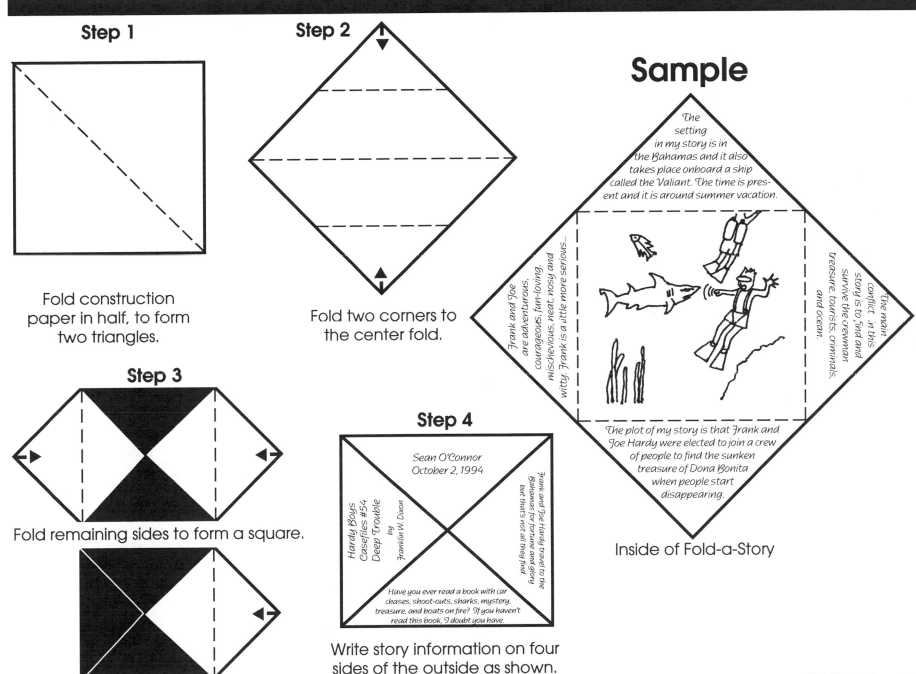

Step 1

Fold construction paper in half, to form two triangles.

Step 2

Fold two corners to the center fold.

Step 3

Fold remaining sides to form a square.

Step 4

Sean O'Connor
October 2, 1994

Hardy Boys
Casefiles #54
Deep Trouble
by
Franklin W. Dixon

Frank and Joe Hardy travel to the Bahamas for fortune and glory but that's not all they find.

Have you ever read a book with car chases, shoot-outs, sharks, mystery, treasure, and boats on fire? If you haven't read this book, I doubt you have.

Write story information on four sides of the outside as shown.

Sample

The setting in my story is in the Bahamas and it also takes place onboard a ship called the Valiant. The time is present and it is around summer vacation.

Frank and Joe are adventurous, courageous, fun-loving, mischevious, neat, nosy and witty. Frank is a little more serious...

The main conflict in this story is to find and survive the crewman treasure, tourists, criminals, and ocean.

The plot of my story is that Frank and Joe Hardy were elected to join a crew of people to find the sunken treasure of Dona Bonita when people start disappearing.

Inside of Fold-a-Story

Story Cube Pop-Up

The story cube pop-up gives new meaning to report writing. Kids have also found it to be an effective presentation tool.

Materials:

Gift box   Markers/pencils/crayons

Scissors   Paper/tagboard

Goal:

To create a story cube with a pop-up object which helps you to retell the story

Steps:

1. Find a square gift box with an attached lid.
2. Draw the story item you want to pop out of the box. Accordion fold a piece of tagboard to glue into the bottom of the box and attach it to the story item.
3. Draw a story scene on the inside box lid.
4. Write the book title, author and your name on the front of the box.
5. Write a story summary on one panel.
6. Draw and write about the main character on the next panel.
7. Draw and write about the setting on the third panel.

Story Cube Pop-Up Example

Drug Store

milford St.

Flag St.

Police Dept
Detective

Chicago
Police

Cop's Kid
by
Scott Corbett

Willie Nelson
October 30, 1994

On a snowy night Chip and Benny were on the way to the store. When they reached the store parking lot, their peaceful night turned into a nightmare. They saw a holdup. A man with a gun was pointing at a bus driver. The bus driver collapsed and the gunman ran straight them he stuck a cigarette reached them he stuck a cigarette into Benny's face. Benny fell clutching his face. The man ran away. The boys knew from that moment they would have to catch the guy who created their nightmare.

Story Retell Poster

A story retell poster captures critical story elements through representative symbols. The poster can become the foundation for a book-talk or a story retell.

Materials:

Colored construction paper (17" x 12") - sheet 1
White construction paper (12" x 9") - sheet 2
Markers/pencils   Glue

Goal:

To create a poster which retells the story through story symbols

Steps:

1. Think through the story.
2. Write the title in the middle of the page.
3. Divide the story into sections (characters, setting, key events).
4. Focus your poster drawings around a character's name or the story title.
5. Center and glue sheet 2 to sheet 1.
6. Use your drawing to retell the story to a friend or your classmates.

Story Retell Poster Example

Retell by Christi Warren

Cereal Box Theater

Kids love to act out the stories they've read. The cereal box theater works well with sponge characters (page 36), and the dialogue projects (see index). It may require adult supervision and help with cutting.

Materials:

Scissors/exacto knife	Markers
Shelf paper/wallpaper	Large cereal box

Goal:

To create a theater for story retellings

Steps:

1. Take the liner out of an empty cereal box. Cut off both sides and the back of the box.
2. Cut a rectangle out of the front of the box.
3. Select shelf paper to cover the cereal box. Place the box on top of the paper's sticky side, leaving at least an inch border.
4. Cut a V-shape above and below the fold lines. Cut out squares in each corner and fold the paper over.
5. Cut the hole out.
6. Turn the theater over and use it to create the retelling of a story.

Cereal Box Theater Directions

Step 1

Take the plastic liner out of an empty cereal box. Cut both sides and the back off.

Step 2

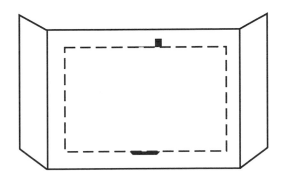

Use an exacto knife to cut a rectangle out of the front side of the cereal box.

Step 3

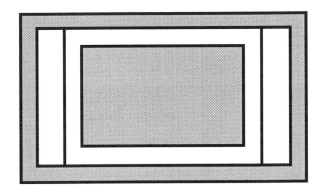

Select shelf paper to cover the cut out cereal box. Leave at least an inch around the outside. Place the box on top of the shelf paper's sticky side.

Step 4

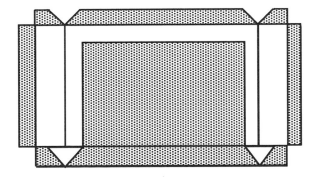

Cut a V shape above and below the fold lines. Cut out squares in each corner. Fold the paper over.

Step 5

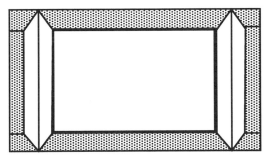

After you've folded the shelf paper over, cut the hole out with an exacto knife.

Step 6

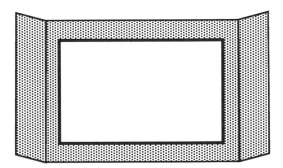

Turn the theater over and use it in the retelling of a story.

Story Newsletter

The story newsletter can take many forms, as shown in the individual and partner examples from Joyce Standing's students.

Materials:

Paper   Pencil/markers
Computer (optional)   Printer (optional)
Newsletter software

Goal:

To create a newsletter based upon a story's plot

Steps:

1. Select a book you will use for the newsletter.
2. Think about the reader. What story information do you want your newsletter to give to readers?
3. Make a list of questions you want to answer in this newsletter.
4. Use the questions to create a first draft. This can be on a computer or by hand.
5. Revise, edit and then create a final copy of the newsletter to share with your friends.

Story Newsletter Examples

Newsletters based on the book
From the Mixed Up Files of Mrs. Basil E. Frankweiler

THE WEEKLY HERALD

that it was bought in Europe

Angel By Michelangelo
by Sandy Stonesifer

This angel is from the Metropolitan Museum of art. It was sold to the museum for $225 by Mrs. Basil E. Frankweiler. She has a private collection that is very large. It used to be kept at her house in New York but that house was closed. The museum's scientists are looking at the statue to determine whether it was done by Michelangelo or not. Their strongest clue remains the M engraved at he base of the statue. This large M is considered a stone mason's mark. Mrs. Frankweiler has told the scientists

Missing
by Sandy Stonesifer

Claudia and Jamie Kincaid are from Greenwich New York. They have been gone for two days. Their parents are frantic. They never arrived at school. Tho police have ruled out kidnapping because Claudia left a note saying not to worry. Claudia is twelve years old and Jamie eight. They are believed to be somewhere in New York city.

Your Mailbox
by Sandy Stonesifer

The Post Office on Martin street's mailboxes are all filled up. The last available mailbox was bought yesterday for approximately four dollars a quarter. Why are all of a sudden so many people buying mailboxes? Well, Sam, a postal worker, says there are more houses that don't have mailboxes now.

Page 1

Newsletter created by Sandy Stonesifer

The Smarcoe Times

Missing Since Friday

A tragic event took place on a Friday in November. A young boy named Jamie and a young girl named Claudia stepped into there school bus and never returned home. They have both been missing for a week now. The kids parents are offering a large amount of money to the person who can provide a clue which could lead to where these kids have gone. People have been making anominous tips which aro so far leading to nothing at all. If these kids have been seen or you know where they are please call 999-9631.

This is a recent family photo.

Jamie - Claudia

Strange sightings in the metropolitan museum.

Recently the metropolitan museum night watch guards have been reporting strange people walking around the old musuem. On watchmen indicated that in pursuit of the figures they will slowly fade away. Another watchman on duty said that he found a young boy about 9 years old in the bathroom. The guard was scared because the boy said that he was an angel from heaven. If you have seen any thing mysterious in the museum please contact the museum. The number is listed in your local phone directory.
Thank you

Newsletter created by Broderick Smith and Matt Marcoe

Candy Box Retell

Eileen Shaner's students at Franconia Elementary in Souderton, PA, enjoy using her book in a box idea. When the box is opened, the story unfolds. This is a great presentation starter.

Materials:

Ruler   Markers/pen(s)

Construction paper   Tape

Candy box   Scissors

Goal:

To create a story summary

Steps:

1. Select the story you want to retell.
2. Determine how many pages you will have in your summary (see example).
3. Measure the box and cut out the pages.
4. Fill in the pages including a title page.
5. Decorate the top of the box as a book cover.
6. Glue the title page to the box cover.
7. Tape the pages together like an accordion.
8. Fold the pages into the box.
9. Use your candy box to retell the story to your friends.

Candy Box Retell Directions

Steps 1 and 2

Select the story you want to retell. Decide what you want to include (words and scenes) and layout your retell on sheets of paper.

Step 3

Measure your box and cut out the number of pages you will need to complete your retell.

Step 4

Create your story retell on the pages you've cut.

Step 5

Decorate the top of the box as a book cover.

Sample

Glue the back of the first page to the box cover, then tape the pages together like an accordion. Fold the pages inside the box and share your project with friends.

First-Person Journal

Martha Ivy and Valerie Marshall use their first-person journal idea with students in their literature circles. Journal writing is an effective way to write and react from the character's perspective.

Materials:

2 tagboard pieces (5 1/2" x 4 1/4")
4-5 sheets of paper   Markers/pencils
Hole punch
Sewn book recipe (page 138)

Goal:

To keep a journal in which you write as if
 you are the character in a story

Steps:

1. Decide the character you want to be in
   your journal.
2. Make the sewn book on page .
3. As the character, write in the journal every
   time you read in the book.
4. Decorate the cover.
5. Share the journal with your friends.

First-Person Journal Example

My Diary

Peter

Number the Stars

written by

Nick Palmer

Today I saw Annemarie and Kristi. It was nice to see them. They remind me of Lisa. I gave them presents and gave their parents a resistance paper. I am worried about soldiers who stopped them on the street.

I'm working on a plan to save Ellen and her parents. The soldiers have trained dogs to find humans. This makes my work more dangerous. So scientists are making a scent to make the dog's sense of smell go away for a few hours.

Non-Fiction Shape Book

Shape books can be used as an alternative to reports. They can also provide a format for giving a presentation in class. Joyce Standing's students used a number of reference books on a topic to create their shape books.

Materials:

Construction paper   White paper
Pens/markers   Stapler
Reference books

Goal:

To record information collected through
  research

Steps:

1. Think about information you've read.
2. Decide upon the shape of your book.
3. List the things you want to include in
   your book (topics).
4. Cut the cover out of construction paper
   and cut the pages out of paper.
5. Draw your cover and write your information on the pages.
6. Staple the cover and pages together.
7. Share your book with friends.

Non-Fiction Shape Book Example

A Book on Slavery
by Kristina Lin

Book Cover

How Began
In the 16th century Spanish colonists forced native Indian populations to work on the land. The Indians could not survive working for the Spanish as slaves and were almost killed. The first blacks landed in Jamestown in 1619. In the later half of the 17th century several blacks were brought to many cities in the north where the slave population grew. In 1800 there were 893,602 in the U.S. Only 36,505 were in the northern states.

Most slaves were brought to the South from different countries. The slaves would have children and they would become slaves also. Many people bought, sold, or traded there slaves. Slaves had no choice.

Rebellion
Many slaves tried to fight against slavery. Some of them led rebellions.
Nat Turner: He was a slave in Virginia that led a rebellion in 1831. He and other slaves tried to escape. In most rebellions the leaders and most of the slaves were caught and killed.
What they didn't have
Slaves didn't have mush of a choice on how they lived. They didn't get to vote, go to public schools, or own property. They had to get their owners written permission to leave the plantions. They also had to have permission from their owners to get married.

Work
Most of the slaves worked on cotton plantions int the South. It was in the United States from 1800 to 1860. Some slaves worked in the house of white slave owners. They cooked, cleaned and helped take care of the slaveowners children, but many of the slaves did planting, raising, and harvesting crops. The slavesin the fields worked from sunrise to sunset.
Living Quarters
Families lived in different huts. There were no bedsteads or furniture. The beds were made of straw and old rags. The owners provided their slaves with the houses they lived in, food they ate, and the clothes they wore.

Story Banner

The story banner helps kids identify significant story objects when giving a book-talk.

Materials:

Coat hanger   Butcher paper

Paint or markers   Glue

Paper/pencil   Glitter

Goal:

To create a banner that uses symbols to represent important story events

Steps:

1. Think through the story you have selected.
2. List important story events. Choose an object (symbol) to represent each event.
3. Draw a draft of your banner on paper.
4. Cut butcher paper to fit the width of a hanger.
5. Fold the paper through the hanger and glue it to itself at the top.
6. Create your banner with paint or markers.
7. Hang up your story banner and retell the story to your friends.

Story Banner Directions

Steps 1, 2 and 3

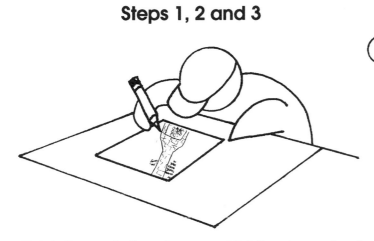

Think through the story and list five important events. Draw objects (symbols) which represent each event. Draw a draft of your banner.

Step 4

Cut a large piece of butcher paper.

Step 5

Fold the paper through the hanger and glue it to itself.

Sample

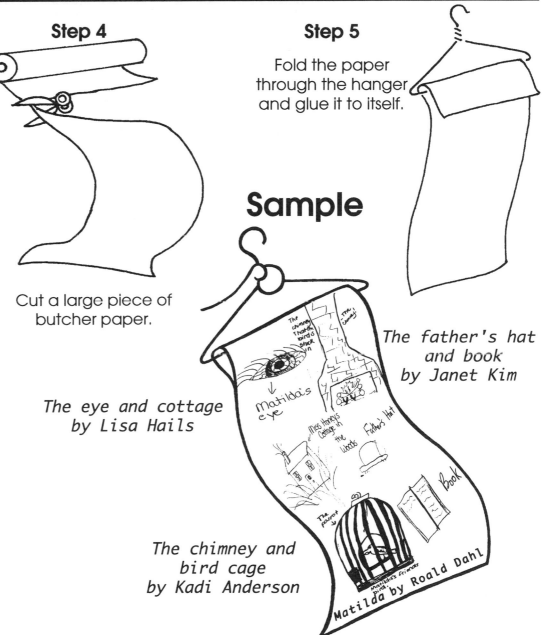

The father's hat and book by Janet Kim

The eye and cottage by Lisa Hails

The chimney and bird cage by Kadi Anderson

Step 6

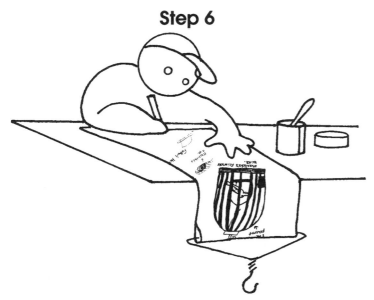

Create your banner with paint or markers.

Hang up your story banner and retell the story to your friends.

Guess the Character Book

Joyce Standing's students enjoyed sharing their Guess the Character books with fellow students. This project can be easily tailored to all ages.

Materials:
Markers/pencils
Book recipes (pages 137-139)

Goal:
To create a book which will enable others who have read the same book to guess each character based on the description

Steps:
1. Select the type of book you want to make from the book recipes (pages 137-139). Follow the instructions.
2. Decide how many characters you want to include from the story.
3. Create a cover and write your introduction on the first page. Write information about each character on right-hand pages. Draw the characters' pictures on left-hand pages.
4. Share your book with friends who have read the story. Can they guess the characters?

Guess the Character Book Example

Guess the Character

by

Andy Meade

Book cover

Introduction to book

This is a guess the character book on "The Call of the Wild." Read the quote from the character and look on the back of the page for their name and picture.

Introduction

I'm the short-tempered dog who doesn't like people walking up to my blind side. My name has a hyphen in the middle. At first I didn't like Buck. He was always getting tangled in the lines and delayed all of us. But after I got used to him, I decided that he was O.K.

right-side page

Sol-Leks

left-side page

I am the previous owner of Buck. He was a good dog, always following me wherever I went. I am also the judge around here. What is my name?

Judge Miller

I gotta whip dem' nuts ta get anyting' outa' dem. My name starts with an "H". Mercedies is my wife and John is my brother-in-law. I run the mail train. Who am I?

Hans

Story Box

A story box is an interesting addition to any book presentation. Just change the story roll and the box can be used over and over to retell many different stories. Adult supervision is required for cutting.

Materials:

Large cardboard box	Exacto knife
White shelf paper roll	Masking tape
Paper towel tubes (2)	Markers

Goal:

To retell the story through a story box

Steps:

1. Cut a large rectangle in the front of the box.
2. Using shelf paper roll, create a story frame (a bit larger than screen) for the book title and for each key event.
3. Draw and cut a hole in the top-left and top-right of the box. Do the same in the bottom of the box (see example).
4. Place the tube ends into the holes.
5. Tape each end of your story roll to a tube.
6. Set the story box on the edge of a desk so the tubes turn easily.
7. Slowly turn the tubes to tell the story.

Story Box Directions

Step 1

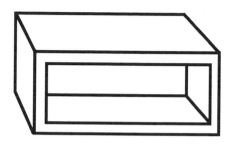

Turn the box on its side and cut a large rectangle in the front. This will become your story box screen.

Step 2

Create story frames slightly larger than the screen on the shelf paper. The title frame is first and 10 story events come next.

Step 3

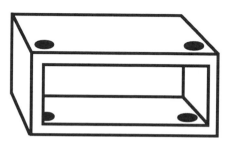

Draw and cut two holes in the top and bottom of the left and right front screen.

Step 4

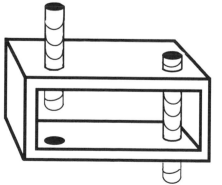

Place the tube ends into the holes.

Step 5

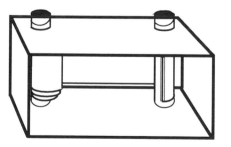

Tape each end of your story roll to a tube.

Step 6

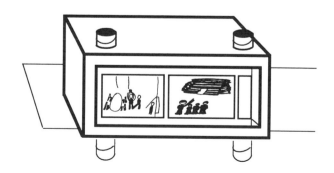

Set the box on the edge of a desk so the tubes turn easily.

☆ My Plot Project Supply Sheet

Name:

My Project is:_____

To do my project I will need:

___ Recipe: _____

    page #:_____

Writing Tools

___ pencil(s)
___ marker(s)
___ pen(s)
___ crayons
___ ruler

Art Supplies

___ glue
___ paste
___ scissors
___ paint
___ paint brush
___ glitter
___ stickers
___ tape
___ clay
___ exacto knife

Paper Supplies

___ form: page #____
___ plain paper
___ lined paper
___ construction paper
___ butcher paper
___ tagboard
___ cardboard
___ shelf paper
___ index card
___ _____
___ _____

Other Possible Items

___ book
___ shoe box
___ reference books
___ hole punch
___ cereal box
___ computer/printer
___ gift box
___ candy box
___ cardboard box
___ hole punch
___ plastic sewing needle
___ yarn/cord
___ coat hanger
___ stapler
___ paper towel tubes

Chapter 6

Project Recipes

Material Recipes

Baker's Clay

page 132

Sugar Cookies

page 133

Papier-Mache Paste

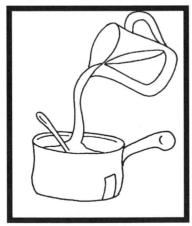

page 134

Modeling Clay

page 135

Book Recipes

Card Book

page 136

Accordion Book

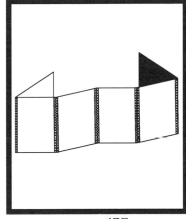

page 137

Sewn Book

page 138

Shape Book

page 139

Baker's Clay

Adult supervision required.

☑ To do this project you will need:

- ❑ Flour (4 cups)
- ❑ Salt (1 cup)
- ❑ Water (11/2 cups)
- ❑ Bowl
- ❑ Spoon
- ❑ Measuring cup
- ❑ Rolling pin
- ❑ Straw
- ❑ Cookie sheet

Step 1

Use a spoon to mix flour, salt and thenwater in a bowl.

Steps 2 and 3

Roll the mixture you've created into a ball. Knead for 5 to 10 minutes until it is smooth.

Step 4

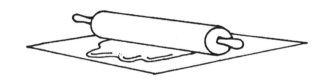

Roll the dough out to a 1/4 inch thickness.

Steps 5 and 6

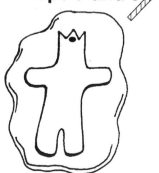

Cut the shapes you want. If you plan to hang the clay objects, use a straw to poke a hole in the top.

Step 7

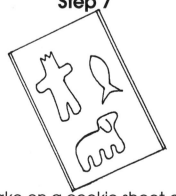

Bake on a cookie sheet at 250 degrees for 2 hours.

Step 8

Let the shapes dry. Paint them and then spray them with clear varnish.

Sugar Cookies

Adult supervision required.

☑ To make this recipe you will need:

- ❑ Powdered Sugar (1 1/2 cups)
- ❑ Butter (1 cup)
- ❑ Egg (1)
- ❑ Vanilla (1 tsp.)
- ❑ Almond Flavoring (1/2 tsp.)
- ❑ Flour (2 1/2 cups)
- ❑ Baking Soda (1 tsp.)
- ❑ Cream of Tartar (1 tsp.)
- ❑ Hand Mixer/Spoons/2 Bowls

Step 1

Mix powdered sugar and butter together until they are creamy and smooth.

Step 2

Add the egg, vanilla and almond flavoring to the mixture. Mix it together well.

Step 3

Mix flour, baking soda and cream of tartar together in another bowl.

Step 4

Add flour mixture to the sugar and butter mixture. Blend until it is creamy and smooth.

Step 5

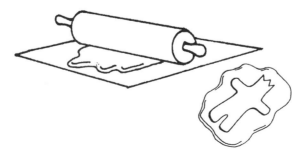

Refrigerate 2-3 hours. Roll dough 1/4 inch thick on lightly floured pastry cloth. Cut to desired shape.

Step 6

Place on lightly greased baking sheet and bake at 375 degrees for 7 to 9 minutes.

Papier-Mache Paste

Adult supervision required.

Step 1

Pour flour and sugar into the pan and stir.

Step 2

Pour the warm water into the flour/sugar mixture.

Step 3

Boil the mixture until it is smooth and clear.

Step 4

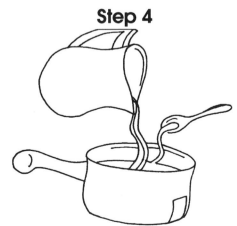

Add the cold water to the mixture to thin it out.

Step 5

Take the pan off the stove. Use the papier-mache paste with projects while it is still warm.

Modeling Clay

Adult supervision required.

☑ To make this recipe you will need:

- ❑ Salt (1/2 cup)
- ❑ Hot Water (1/2 cup)
- ❑ Cornstarch (1/2 cup)
- ❑ Cold Water (1/4 cup)
- ❑ Stove
- ❑ Bowl/Spoons
- ❑ Saucepan (1medium)
- ❑ Measuring cup (1)

Step 1

Pour salt and hot water in a pan. Heat and stir until it boils.

Step 2

Pour the cornstarch in a bowl. Add cold water and stir.

Step 3

Add the cornstarch mixture to the boiling water. Stir it vigorously.

Step 4

Cook mixture over low heat, stirring continuously until it is stiff. Then let it cool.

Step 5

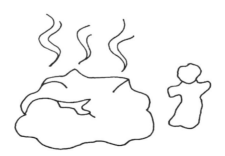

Knead clay until it's smooth. Create shapes out of it.

Step 6

Let shapes dry 1-2 days and paint them.

Card Book

Step 1

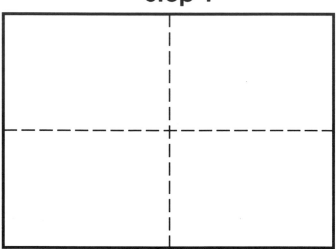

Sheet of white paper.

Step 2

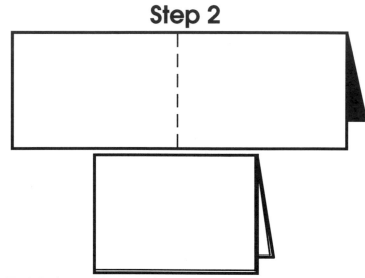

Fold sheet in half and then in half again.

Step 3

Turn the paper around so it opens like a card.

Accordion Book

Step 1

Trace your page shape onto
the tagboard.

Step 2

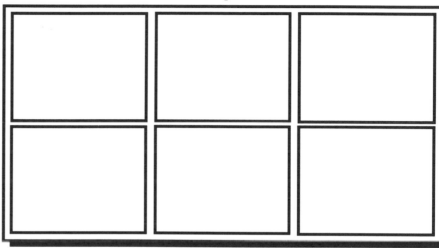

Cut out your book pieces.

Step 3

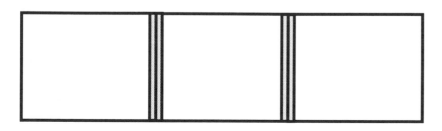

Tape pieces together on the front and
back of the tagboard.

Sewn Book

To make this recipe you will need:
- 2 tagboard pieces (5 1/2" x 4 1/4")
- Hole punch
- Pencil/markers
- Yarn or cord
- Paper
- Plastic sewing needle

Steps 1 and 2

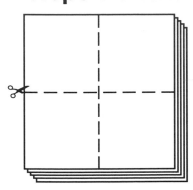

Fold paper two ways and cut into fourths.

Step 3

(5 1/2" x 4 1/4")

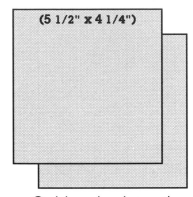

Cut two tagboard pieces for the cover.

Step 4

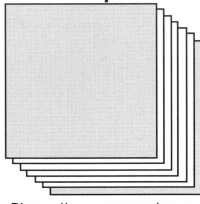

Place the covers above and below the pages.

Step 5

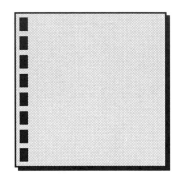

Punch holes in the stacked pieces.

Step 6

Cut a 33 1/2" piece of yarn.

Step 7

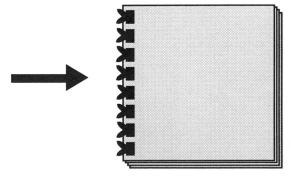

Starting at the bottom, loop yarn around the holes. Continue looping from the top back down. Tie the loose ends.

Shape Book

Step 1

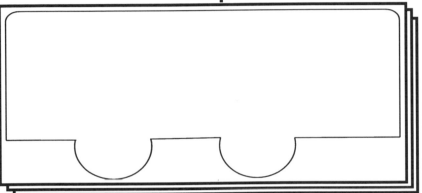

Decide how many pages you want in your book.
Draw a shape on construction paper.

Step 2

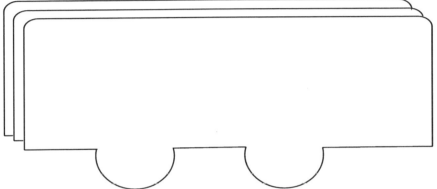

Cut out the cover and book pages into
the shape you've chosen.

Step 3

Draw the cover of your book. Staple the cover and
pages together. Use it in the project you've selected.

Project Recipe Cards

Baker's Clay Recipe Card*

You will need...
- ❑ Flour (4 cups)
- ❑ Salt (1 cup)
- ❑ Water (1 1/2 cups)
- ❑ Oven (250 degrees)
- ❑ Bowl (1)
- ❑ Spoon (1)
- ❑ Straw (1)
- ❑ Measuring Cup (1)

1. Mix flour, salt and then water in a bowl with a spoon.
2. Roll the mixture you've created into a ball.
3. Knead the ball for 5-10 minutes until it is very smooth.
4. Roll the dough out to a 1/4 inch thickness.
5. Cut dough into the shapes you want.
6. To hang the shape, create a hole in top with a straw.
7. Bake at 250 degrees for 2 hours.
8. Let cool. Paint shapes and spray on clear varnish.

* Adult supervision is required for young children

Sugar Cookie Recipe Card*

You will need...
- ❑ Powdered Sugar (1 1/2 cups)
- ❑ Vanilla (1 tsp.)
- ❑ Butter (1 cup)
- ❑ Egg (1)
- ❑ Almond Flavoring (1/2 tsp.)
- ❑ Measuring cup
- ❑ Baking Soda (1 tsp.)
- ❑ Cream of Tartar (1 tsp.)
- ❑ Flour (2 1/2 cups)
- ❑ Hand Mixer/Spoons
- ❑ Bowls (2)

1. Mix powdered sugar and butter together in bowl 1 until creamy and smooth.
2. Add the egg, vanilla and almond flavoring. Mix well.
3. Mix flour, baking soda, and cream of tartar in bowl 2.
4. Add flour mixture to sugar/butter mixture and blend.
5. Refrigerate 2-3 hours. Roll dough 1/4" thick. Cut shapes.
6. Bake at 375 degrees on lightly greased baking sheet.

* Adult supervision is required for young children

Papier-Mache Paste Recipe Card*

You will need...
- ❑ Flour (2 cups)
- ❑ Sugar (1/2 cup)
- ❑ Warm Water (1/2 gallon)
- ❑ Spoon
- ❑ Cold Water (1/2 quart)
- ❑ Pan (1 medium size)
- ❑ Measuring cup (1)
- ❑ Stove

1. Pour flour and sugar into the pan and stir.
2. Pour the warm water into the flour/sugar mixture.
3. Boil the mixture until it is smooth and clear.
4. Add the cold water to the mixture to thin it out.
5. Take pan off the stove and use the papier-mache paste with projects while it is still warm.

* Adult supervision is required for young children

Modeling Clay Recipe Card*

You will need...
- ❑ Salt (1/2 cup)
- ❑ Cornstarch (1/2 cup)
- ❑ Hot Water (1/2 cup)
- ❑ Cold Water (1/4 cup)
- ❑ Paint
- ❑ Bowl/Spoons
- ❑ Pan (1 medium size)
- ❑ Measuring cup (1)
- ❑ Stove

1. Pour salt and hot water in pan and stir to boiling.
2. Pour cornstarch in a bowl, add cold water and stir.
3. Add the cornstarch mixture into the boiling water. Stir the mixture vigorously.
4. Cook mixture over low heat, stirring continuously until stiff. Then let it cool.
5. Knead clay until it's smooth. Create shapes out of it.
6. Let shapes dry (1-2 days) and paint them.

* Adult supervision is required with young children

Chapter 7

Reference Books

Reference Books

Author	Book Title	Publisher
Brown, Hazel Cambourne, Brian	*Read and Retell*	Heinemann Educational Books, 1990
Calkins, Lucy McCormick	*Lessons from a Child*	Heinemann Educational Books, 1983
Johnson, Terry D. Louis, Daphne R.	*Literacy through Literature*	Heinemann Educational Books, 1987
Lukens, Rebecca J.	*A Critical Handbook of Children's Literature*	HarperCollins Publishers, 1990
Norton, Donna	*The Impact of Literature-Based Reading*	Macmillan Publishing Company, 1992
O'Brien-Palmer, Michelle	*Book-Write: A Creative Bookmaking Guide for Young Authors*	MicNik Publications, Inc., 1992
O'Brien-Palmer, Michelle	*Book-Talk: Exciting Literature Experiences for Kids*	MicNik Publications, Inc., 1993
O'Brien-Palmer, Michelle	*Read & Write: Fun Literature and Writing Connections for Kids*	MicNik Publications, Inc., 1994
Rothlein, Liz Meinbach, Anita Meyer	*The Literature Connection*	Scott, Foresman and Company, 1991

Chapter 8

Forms

Book Train

Me

My name is _____

I read this book!

A picture of my favorite character

Title _____

Today's date _____

Forms from *I Love to Read*, from © MicNik Publications, Inc.

CHARACTER PROJECT

The character project I chose was:

_____

The book I read was:

_____

❑ I enjoyed this project
❑ I didn't enjoy this project

My Signature: _____

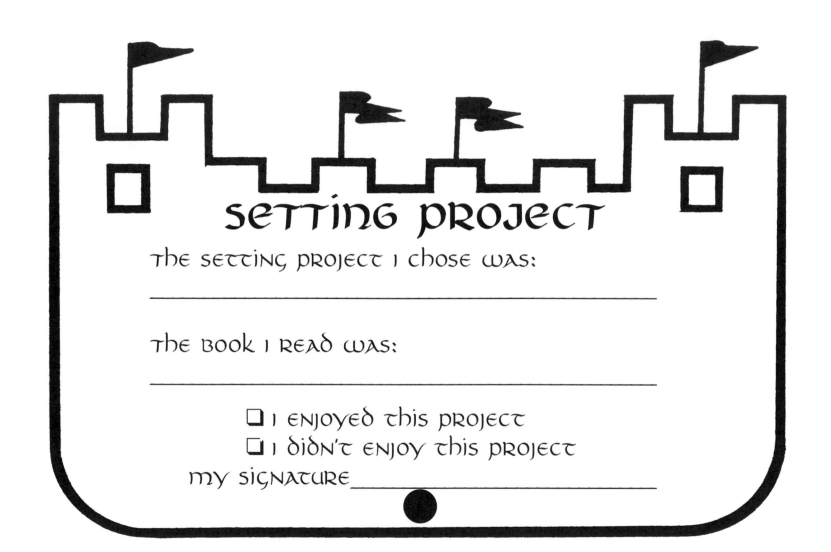

SETTING PROJECT

THE SETTING PROJECT I CHOSE WAS:

_____

THE BOOK I READ WAS:

_____

❑ I ENJOYED THIS PROJECT
❑ I DIDN'T ENJOY THIS PROJECT
MY SIGNATURE_____

PLOT PROJECT

THE PLOT PROJECT I CHOSE WAS:

_____

THE BOOK I READ WAS:

_____

☐ I ENJOYED THIS PROJECT
☐ I DIDN'T ENJOY THIS PROJECT

MY SIGNATURE:_____

My Beginning, Middle, and End Book

My Favorite Character

Story: _____

My name: _____

This happened in the **beginning**...

This happened in the **middle**...

This happened in the **end**...

Chapter 9

Project Index

I LOVE TO READ Projects

Page	Project	Character	Setting	Plot	Book	Material	Younger	Older	Multi-age	Simple	Complex	Individual	Partner	Group	Art	Writing	Dialogue	Recycling	Report	Book-Talk	Retelling
		Project			Recipe		Age			Type									Uses		
36	Sponge Character	●					●				●	●			●						●
38	Talking Character	●		●			●				●	●			●	●	●	●		●	
40	Character Sculpture	●				●			●		●	●			●			●		●	●
42	Bean Bag Character	●							●		●	●			●			●			●
44	Cookie Characters	●				●			●		●	●		●	●						
46	Story Flip Book	●	●	●			●			●		●	●			●			●	●	
48	Char. Accordion Book	●	●	●	●				●	●		●	●		●	●				●	●
50	Character Magnets	●							●		●	●	●		●					●	
52	Character Trait Box	●	●	●					●	●		●	●		●	●				●	
54	Thumbprint Char.'s	●					●			●		●	●		●	●	●			●	
56	Pop-Up Dialogue	●	●	●					●		●	●	●		●		●			●	●
58	Biography Monologue	●		●				●			●	●	●			●			●	●	
60	Character Mask	●				●			●		●	●	●		●			●		●	●
62	Meet the Characters	●		●	●				●	●		●	●		●	●			●	●	
68	Story Stones	●	●						●	●		●			●			●			●
70	Triorama		●						●	●		●	●	●	●						
72	Setting Map		●						●	●		●	●		●					●	
74	Simple Diorama		●						●	●		●	●		●			●		●	
76	Sculpted Diorama		●					●			●	●	●		●			●		●	
78	Shoebox Story Scene		●						●		●	●			●			●		●	
80	Magnetic Story Frame		●						●		●	●			●					●	
82	Story Props		●	●					●	●		●	●	●	●	●		●		●	●
84	Magnetic Story Map		●						●	●		●	●	●	●				●	●	●
86	Literature Postcards	●	●	●					●	●			●		●	●					
88	Story Snow Scene		●						●	●		●	●	●	●			●		●	●
90	Story Neighborhood		●						●		●	●	●	●	●			●		●	●
92	Reader's Theater		●						●	●		●	●		●						●
94	Storyboard																				

I LOVE TO READ Projects

Page	Project	Character	Setting	Plot	Book	Material	Younger	Older	Multi-age	Simple	Complex	Individual	Partner	Group	Art	Writing	Dialogue	Recycling	Report	Book-Talk	Retelling
		Project			**Recipe**		**Age**			**Type**									**Uses**		
100	Beg., Middle & End	●	●	●	●		●			●		●	●		●	●					●
102	Story Time Capsule			●				●			●	●	●		●			●	●	●	●
104	Story Pop-Out	●	●	●					●	●		●			●	●		●	●	●	
106	Fold-a-Story	●	●	●					●	●		●			●	●			●	●	
108	Story Cube Pop-Up	●		●					●		●	●	●		●	●			●	●	
110	Story Retell Poster		●	●					●	●		●	●	●	●					●	●
112	Cereal Box Theater			●					●		●	●	●		●			●			●
114	Story Newsletter	●	●	●					●	●		●	●	●	●	●	●		●	●	●
116	Candy Box Retell	●		●					●		●	●	●		●			●			●
118	First-Person Journal	●		●	●				●		●	●	●		●	●			●	●	●
120	Non-Fiction Shape Bk.	●		●	●				●		●	●	●		●	●			●	●	
122	Story Banner			●			●			●		●	●	●				●		●	●
124	Guess the Character	●		●	●				●		●	●	●		●	●			●	●	
126	Story Box			●					●		●	●	●		●			●	●	●	●

Index

Index

Index

Index

Index

ABOUT THE AUTHOR
Of...

**I LOVE TO READ
READ & WRITE
BOOK-TALK
BOOK-WRITE
THROUGH MY EYES
BOOK-TALK CASSETTE**

Michelle received her undergraduate and graduate degrees at the University of Washington. Michelle is 40 years old and lives in the Pacific Northwest with her son and husband. She is an educational consultant and speaker. Michelle always includes children in the creation of her books and tapes.

WORKSHOPS AND ASSEMBLIES

for more information, please call (206) 881-6476/fax: (206) 885-2133 or write to
MicNik Publications, Inc. • P.O. Box 3041 • Kirkland, WA 98083

WORKSHOPS FOR TEACHERS
Book-Talk and Book-Write

Presented by...
Michelle O'Brien-Palmer

Practical ideas from real classrooms:

Book-Talk
- *Bringing literature into your classroom*
- *Starting your own literature circles*
- *Prediction, retelling, and reviewing strategies*
- *Reading projects recommended by kids*

Book-Write
- *The 5-Step Writing Process in action*
- *Setting, character, and plot development*
- *Great bookmaking ideas*
- *Journal starters and fun writing projects*

WORKSHOPS FOR KIDS
Read & Write

Presented by...
Michelle O'Brien-Palmer
Interactive Workshops for K-6th*
can include...

- 5-Step Writing Process
- Genre – book selection
- Story elements
- Character developement
- Setting development
- Plot development
- Book-making
- Fun projects

*Workshops are tailored to the needs of each classroom.

ASSEMBLIES FOR SCHOOLS
Book-Talk and Book-Write

Featuring:
Michelle O'Brien-Palmer — *Author*
Heidi Stephens — *Illustrator*
Nancy Stewart — *Musician*

Drop Everything and Read!
A musical celebration of books and readers. Selections include; I Love the Library, Genre Tree, Hello Fiction, Remarkable Reviewers, and many more.

I'm An Author and So Are You!
A musical celebration of young authors and writing. Selections include; Just 5-Steps, Make a Book, Every Story Has..., I Want to Be An Illustrator, and many more.

MicNik Publications, Inc.

Book-Talk does for reading what *Book-Write* does for writing. It is a fun, clear, easy-to-follow resource guide for teachers and parents who want to encourage a lifelong love of literature. *Book-Talk* is filled with real kids' examples and reproducible forms.

11" x 81/2" • 160 pages • $16.95
ISBN 1-879235-02-1

A fun, easy-to-follow, bookmaking guide for young authors. Filled with examples of other young authors' books. A wonderful resource for teachers and parents interested in the writing process. Reproducible forms for use in the classroom or at home.

11" x 81/2" • 128 pages • $16.95
ISBN 1-879235-01-3

A look at life through the eyes of a young child. Co-authored and illustrated by children – the poetry in *Through My Eyes* has brought joy to readers all over the country. There is space for young authors to write their own poems in the back of this book.

5 1/2" x 81/2" • 33 pages • $6.95
ISBN 1-879235-00-5

CASSETTE

BOOK-TALK (Cassette)
Singable Songs for Lifelong Readers

Combining music, learning and fun, this tape captures the essence of literature for young readers (K-4th). Starting with an inspiring and unforgettable tune called *Drop Everything and Read*, BOOK-TALK is a musical celebration of literature and readers. Alone, or as a companion to the book, this tape is an excellent resource for classrooms and home.

$9.95, ISBN 1-879235-03-X

A great resource guide which invites children (K-6th), teachers and parents to explore and experience the dynamic connections between reading and writing. The young authors blossom as they link the books they are reading to their own wriitng. Fun projects recommended by kids and reproducible forms are included. Great for home and school.

11" x 81/2" • 160 pages • $16.95
ISBN 1-879235-04-8